OF STARS AND MEN

OF STARS AND MEN

The Human Response to an Expanding Universe

HARLOW SHAPLEY

REVISED EDITION · **BEACON PRESS** · **BOSTON**

DESIGNED AND ILLUSTRATED BY RICHARD C. BARTLETT

Contents

Foreword

The present treatise is not written for astronomical or other scientific technicians. It is therefore presented with few bibliographic references, and except for parts of Chapters 6, 7, and 10 it is essentially free of technicalities. When I use the phrase "Cosmic Facts," the reader is asked not to assume too rigid a meaning for the word "facts"; what is considered factual today is tomorrow recognized as capable of further refinement. The occasional repetitions of argument and phrasing in the later chapters are not oversights; they are meant to emphasize points where emphasis seems advisable.

I should record my thanks to Mrs. Shapley, who has patiently discussed details of thought and diction and assisted with the preparation of the manuscript.

If this book were to be dedicated to its first and chief encouragement is should probably salute starlight, insects, the galaxies, and the fossil plants and animals, since they have joined in inciting the analysis and attitudes herein recorded.

HARLOW SHAPLEY

OF STARS AND MEN

Introduction—Nothing Merely Human

To build from rough materials a rational and stable structure that contains man and his universe is the ambitious goal of this writing and of the underlying studies. A considerable amount of old structure has been pulled down in recent years. Further demolition is advisable. In particular we must continue to jettison much human vanity and many anthropocentric arguments. And we should expect that our present reconstruction may also need revising in the not very distant future. Of necessity we must work in our times and for our times. We must use the concepts and methods now available and those that can be logically developed.

Stated otherwise, the purpose of this small volume is to present some information and ideas, new and old, bearing on the position of mankind in the universe of physics and sensation. It is an essay on orientation, including a tentative obituary, one might say, of anthropocentrism in our description of the universe.

A survey of the relevant knowledge that the inquiring mind of man has brought to light naturally leads to speculative meditation, to a dreaming built out of wonderment, to a groping for both an objective and an introspective philosophy. But for the most part I shall present here only the raw materials and their more obvious implications. They are to be used by the reader as he will for his orientation in the material world, and possibly in the non-material. It will be a cooperative project — writer and reader, reporter and critic.

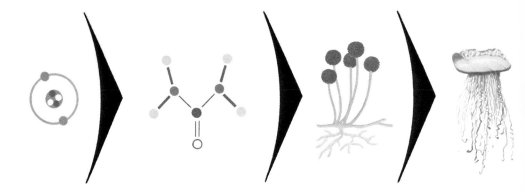

For example, I shall emphasize the continuity in the series of living organisms — the long continuous series from the inorganic molecules, through the complex organic molecular aggregates, to the primitive plants and animals; then on through the myriads of more complex biological forms to the higher types of man — an evolution through a billion years or more. This physical continuity will be stressed; readers may suggest, if they will, where "spirit" appears to enter the stream of life. I shall present the expanding universe of galaxies; others may suggest what started it off and why.

We are undertaking, in this essay on star facts and human destiny, a serious enterprise. Destiny has an ominous sound and facts are frequently disturbing and oppressive. To postpone a possible depression about our role or function in the stellar universe, and to evade for a time the heavier implications of man's physical position, we shall first emphasize briefly the good features of life under the present constellations. We shall begin this essay in an optimistic vein; later there will be time and need for a more sombre look.

It is a good world for many of us. Nature is reasonably benign, and good will is a common human trait. There is widespread beauty, pleasing symmetry, collaboration, lawfulness, progress — all qualities that appeal to man-the-thinker if not always to man-the-animal. When not oppressed by hunger or cold or man-made indignities we are inclined toward contentment, sometimes toward lightheartedness.

But rather than a lighthearted and somewhat evasive view of our situation and responsibilities, it would be more in keeping with what lies ahead to adopt from the beginning the attitude of mature inquirers, and confront the cosmic facts squarely and fully: small but magnificent man face to face with enormous and magnificent universe.

The first step is to ask a preliminary question and provide a synoptic answer. The question is "What is the Cosmos?"

Four or More Basic Entities

The scientists who busy themselves with thoughts and researches on the total universe, and also some philosophers whose coverage includes cosmology, are soon led to the conclusion that the physical universe consists of, or is amply described by, or is presented to our knowledge through, four recognizable basic entities — entities that can be named and to some extent isolated. There may be more than four. But, for the sake of simplicity, we are tempted to put all the world of physics, and perhaps all the biological world, into the framework of these four properties. They are, of course, Space, Time, Matter, and Energy. Many quasi-entities are recognized, such as motion, velocity, metabolism, entropy, creation — but they are derivatives, or are combinations among the four.

Although not yet recognized or isolated, may there not be other basic entities, perhaps some of superior importance? In particular, is there some other property of the material world that is necessary to make the universe go or develop? Something like Motion in an abstract sense? To put the question in personal terms: If you were given the four basic entities and full power, opportunity, and desire, could you construct a universe out of space, time, matter, and energy? Or would you require a fifth entity — another basic property or action?

We seem to belabor this point, but the somewhat mystical fifth entity must be referred to more than once in what follows. That it exists we can hardly doubt. Is it a master entity, perhaps more basic than space and matter and possibly including them — something quite unlike the four named above?* Is it indispensable? Something that would make click a universe of stars, organisms, and natural laws, that might otherwise be clickless?

*We can, if we choose, combine the four in pairs: space-time and matter-energy, and search for a third basic entity, rather than a fifth.

At this point some readers may be thinking of the word and concept "God," but we should not be hasty with such a deep and critical thought. Let us not use up that important and comprehensive concept for only a part of the universe, or something already comprehensible to primitive us. Working in the field of Cosmography† we are tantalized by the possibility that hidden world characteristics do exist for which there may be an independent world-dynamic, one that we could call Direction, Form, Drive, the Will of Omnipotence, or Consciousness. But if it be Drive or Consciousness, the concept must be of cosmic extent. It must touch galaxies and viruses. Nothing that is only terrestrial has a rightful place in Cosmography.

What? How? Why?

Already in the preceding pages we have revealed our limited knowledge of the world. It is amazing how little we know compared with what we conceive as ultimately within our reach. And how small is that reachable part compared with what is beyond! Superstition and loyalty to dogmas have kept us bogged down not far above the most primitive views of the universe. Fancy how far we might now have gone if we had not been shackled by mythology and by certain social conventions and national policies. What intellectual progress we might have made by this time if we had emphasized the psyche rather than property! Eventually we may not be as poorly equipped as we are now to answer three basic questions:

What is the universe?   How does it work?   Why is the universe?

To the first question —"What?"— we can respond in an elementary way, and produce a brave partial answer, mumbling something about matter, gravitation, time, and protoplasm. To the second question —"How?"— we

† In rough definition, Cosmography is to the Cosmos what geography is to the earth.

venture something about the laws of nature, the death of heat, and the running away of the galaxies. But to the question, "Why is the universe?" we are likely to exclaim, "God only knows!"— and apparently that knowledge is "restricted." Being somewhat incorrigible in matters cosmic, we begin to ask ourselves why the "Why" of the universe is restricted, and why we should accept the suggestion that the now deep and distant mysteries must remain forever in the secret category. Many of the unexplainables that baffled the ancients are for us commonplace rational facts or operations. The element of mystery has evaporated from them. If we continue to work hard, to think clearly and deeply, will not some of the major "Why's" of the universe become answerable by us? Philosophers would probably say "No!" but I let the question stand.

Plan of the Discussion

In order to present the principal arguments in a relatively short essay, I propose to restrict the discussion to a few steps in the adjustment of our minds and acts to what I like to call the Cosmic Facts. The steps we shall take are the following:

1. An examination of the need for a new consideration of man's place and function, if any, in the cosmos. Are there good reasons why we should now disturb our meager peace of mind because of what science is trying to tell us? The answer is "Yes, decidedly so." We should face the revised specifications of our job and the new indications of our potentialities.

2. The locating of the earth (and mankind) in the physical universe which we deduce from sensory data and reasoning. The search is built around the basic entities; we search out our place not only in space but in time, matter, and energy. "Is man in a commanding position," we ask, "or in the ranks, or just tagging along, forgotten of the stars from which he sprang?" We shall show that his physical location is now definitely determined and that in a rather peculiar far-fetched sense he is not wholly insignificant.

3. The problems associated with the origin of the earth and with the number and distribution of life-bearing plants.

4. The question of the nature and distribution of sentient life. Is it a local operation, developed under special circumstances on or near the surface of this one planet, or is it a widespread activity?

5. The Fourth Adjustment in our knowledge of the location of earth-bound man. From his primeval egocentrism in a hostile environment he has developed a view of the universe that is more in keeping with the astronomical and biological evidence. The Hostility of Nature is no longer a useful concept.

6. A consideration of the Generic Mind, and a preliminary exploration among the sense organs which are our tools of comprehension, and are suitable for cosmographic investigation.

7. Finally, some suggestions are offered about the future of man as a dominant terrestrial animal. This is a fertile field for guessing and also for hope and despair, for satisfaction and doubt. We are led to thoughts on the extinction of the species and also to a consideration of human survival programs and the ethical attitudes based thereon.

We have named four basic entities of the physical world and have opened the door to a consideration of the structure and meaning of life. In preparation for such an inquiry I have placed before the reader the scaffolding, or at least the rough blueprints, of a cosmic castle. In the following chapters I must fill in details. We shall arrive at no completely finished structure. I am not wholly certain whether we are working on the foundation or on the roof. More likely, and this is our modest ambition, we are working on an effective toolhouse that must precede the ultimate structure.

How might we name the edifice with which as Cosmographers we concern ourselves? It is not Science in the standard sense. Is it metaphysics, religion, human grasping, resignation, hope? Provisionally we might call it "Adjustment through Understanding."

CHAPTER TWO

New Bottles for New Wines

We shall start our account with the following question: Is there not at this time a justification for a revised look at mankind as a world factor? "Yes!" is our prompt answer. To the scientist, rich in new knowledge, and to the puzzled layman, and perhaps to some philosophers, the answer is decidedly affirmative. An elementary reason for a reconsideration lies in the recognition in recent years of the "displacement" of the sun, earth, and other planets from a central place, or even a significant place, in the sidereal universe — in the placing of the observer in a very undistinguished location in a faint spiral arm of an ordinary galaxy.

This reason is elementary but momentous, for it concerns the replacement of the earlier *geocentric* and *heliocentric* theories of the universe by the *eccentric* arrangement that we now all accept. By this move we have made a long forward step in cosmic adjustment — a step that is unquestionably irreversible. We must get used to the fact that we are peripheral, that we move along with our star, the sun, in the outer part of a galaxy that is one among billions of star-rich galaxies.

If there is some special grandeur in our position in space and time, I fail to find it. Our glory if any must lie elsewhere. Also, should we not openly question the rather vain and tedious dogma that man somehow is something very remarkable, something superior? He may be. I hope that he is. But certainly it is not in his location in space, or in his times; not in his energy content or chemical composition. He is not at all outstanding in the four basic entities — space, time, matter, energy. There is nothing unique, and worthy of boast, in his size, activity, or even his epoch in cosmic chronology. He is not at the beginning of things, nor at the end.

Man is, of course, an intricate and interesting phenomenon, but we should not get sentimental about him, or introspective, until later chapters,

and then only with restraint. Once we have cleared away some of our illusions about man's worldly importance, we shall be better prepared to consider the position of the human mind and estimate its power, its significance, and its effectiveness in grasping cosmic situations.

Egocentrism and anthropomorphic bias have long dominated our thoughts and clouded our deductions. Perhaps this is inevitable. We are human and cannot be purely objective. We have to know the world through our own sense organs. The cosmic outlooks of beetles, or protons, or comets are not easy for us to conjure up and wisely exploit. We must admit, however, that the subjective approach — the thinking and acting always in terms of self or of mankind — has grave limitations. It is full of traps. Objectivity is the only brush with which to paint a true and satisfying picture of the cosmos and a clear and clean sketch of its relationship to our experiment in humanity.

The presumed superiority of man as an animal; the assumption of the importance of life, especially of human life, to the universe at large; and the insistence and feeling that our moment in the geological ages is somehow enormously significant in the flow of time — all these easy postulates should be questioned. To attain a proper evaluation of the interpreter measured against the interpreted and to counter somewhat our automatic egocentrism, we may need to overemphasize the role of galaxies and stars, those "cold fires, yet with power to burn and brand his nothingness into man."

There should be, however, nothing very humiliating about our material inconsequentiality. Are we debased by the greater speed of the sparrow, the larger size of the hippopotamus, the keener hearing of the dog, the finer detectors of odors possessed by insects? We can easily become adjusted to all these evidences of our inferiority and maintain a feeling of importance and well-being. We should also take the stars in our stride; we should adjust ourselves to the cosmic facts. It is a magnificent universe in which to play a part, however humble.

Many distinguished human voices of the past have spoken dispassionately of delicate man defending himself against the cold of the universe. A few have ended in puzzled despair. Some have come to the conclusion that thinking man has been miscast in the cosmic drama: for he has so much to work with yet finds himself cramped in the little solar system, short-lived, and enslaved by both animal habits inherited from the primeval jungle and dogmas acquired from his immediate ancestors.

Although some inquirers have kept themselves wide-eyed and have remained hopeful that the limited mind of man can successfully cope with the problems of the universe, many of the meditators, perhaps most of them, soon or late, retreat to the solace of dogmatic theology.

We are now able to interpret the world in a way more circumstantial and rational than it could be interpreted by Moses, Lucretius, Spinoza, or Pascal, whose cosmologies were geocentric or heliocentric and limited. We have deep knowledge and much critical information that was not available to the philosophers of earlier centuries. We have gone far, very far, in the accumulation of verifiable facts. And this we must remember: there will be, if we remain civilized, no return. We must henceforth live with our scientific acquisitions. No amount of skepticism about details, no sweeping denials of observation, no distortion of the recent revelations of science can erase the intellectual progress. Wishing will not revive the dear dead hypotheses.

A Brief Digression on Arithmetic

The Macrocosmos is so large and the elementary particles in the Microcosmos so small that the intercomparisons of dimensions, such as are relevant in the table of material organizations (Table I of Chapter 4), are cumbersome. To write down in numbers our estimates of the quantity of fundamental particles in the space-time universe would require 80 or 90 figures — a labor to write and a concept almost impossible to grasp. A galaxy is a million million million million times the size of an amoeba, and an amoeba is a giant compared with an electron. Similarly, we have cumbersome comparisons when dealing with the time entity. For example, the ratio of the rotation period of a spiral galaxy to the vibration period of an ammonia molecule is greater than ten million billion billion. We need a simpler mode of expressing large numbers.

To escape the impressive but clumsy numbering, we may resort to the use of "power" arithmetic, expressing large and small numbers in terms of the powers of the number ten. It is a very simple device, as well as convenient. The second power of ten, that is 10^2, is 100. A thousand is 10^3, and a thousandth is 10^{-3}. A million is 10^6, and a millionth is 10^{-6}. A trillion is 10^9, and so on. The number of atoms in a gram of hydrogen is 6×10^{23}, which is six followed by twenty-three zeros. The approximate age of the earth's crust is 5×10^9 years — that is, 5000 million years; 3×10^{10} is the velocity of light in centimeters per second; 10^{-30} grams per cubic centimeter is a value for the average density of matter in metagalactic space. This number, 10^{-30}, is obviously a much neater expression than 1 over 1,000,000 followed by twenty-three more zeros.

To multiply such large numbers we simply *add* the exponents: $10^{14} \times 10^{12} = 10^{26}$. If there are coefficients they are simply *multiplied*: $2 \times 10^7 \times 3.1 \times 10^7 = 6.2 \times 10^{14}$, which is the number of seconds in 20 million years.

To divide we subtract exponents: $10^{16} \div 10^2 = 10^{14}$. Additions and subtractions are obvious operations, though infrequently used in power arithmetic: $2.4 \times 10^7 + 0.15 \times 10^7 = 2.55 \times 10^7$.

Preview of the Argument

The advance of knowledge in the scientific realm (science widely defined) and our currently greater freedom from theological dogmas have opened up channels of analysis and avenues of thought which, if then known, would have altered profoundly the theories of the cosmologists of earlier years, and certainly would have affected their considerations of First Causes. The new discoveries about life, matter, and space should be and generally are recognized as relevant to philosophy. They can be extensively documented and convincingly presented. But here it should suffice to cite without much elaboration several of the direction-bending developments. They might be called ego-shrinking revelations. Most of them will be detailed in subsequent chapters.

1. Naturally I start with the stars and note that the number now within our scientific knowledge is not the five or six thousand naked-eye objects of the ancient Hindus and Greeks, nor the million stars revealed by the small telescopes in the days of Galileo and Newton, nor the few billion of a generation ago. The number of stars in today's surveys is more than 10^{20} — more than a hundred thousand million billion — and each star radiates the fuel for life to whatever planets go along in the journey through the depths of space and the eons of time. In the orientation of man and his works in the material universe the implications of that vast number are obvious.

0,000,000,000,000,000,000,000

2. No longer is the origin of life a deep mystery. Supernatural "intervention" in the biochemical operation that we call life is not required. Natural operations, most of them already known, will suffice. We have bridged, at least provisionally, the gap between life and the lifeless. The microbiologist probing down from organic cells toward the inanimate corpuscles (atoms and electrons) and the chemist moving up from the atoms toward the animate organisms are practically in contact. Much detailed work, however, remains to be done. The approaches to the bridge need careful building, the superstructure must be strengthened, the flooring filled in. The leading workmen in the transformation of the lifeless to the living, i.e., the chemist and the biologist, have assistance from the geologist analyzing fossiliferous rocks; from the astronomer, who finds evidence for a long-enduring pre-Cambrian age; from the statistician, who shows that even the very improbable may happen in the course of cosmic time, including such improbables as the "accidental" synthesis of amino acids, when times are long and materials abundant. New procedures, new facts, new conclusions are here involved. In Chapter 10 this situation is further explored.

3. Knowledge of the brevity of our Psychozoic era in the evolutionary history of terrestrial biology, and awareness of the peripheral situation of the earth in our galaxy, have now, or soon will have, one very useful consequence; namely, that thinking man's egotism is, or soon will be, under control so satisfactorily that he can look at the whole of creation more objectively than heretofore. He has no need or right to remain only earth-minded.

4. The probably great abundance throughout the universe of highly developed forms of life, including nerve-guided beings, indicates that we must accept ourselves and our fellow biota as only one assemblage of the biological developments, and in all likelihood not the highest development, whatever "highest" means. Because life, we shall later argue, inevitably emerges and evolves wherever the chemistry, geology, and climatology are right.

5. The high probability of the existence of senses and sense organs now unknown to man is proposed. Their existence seems indeed so reason-

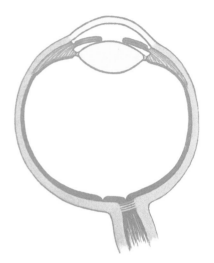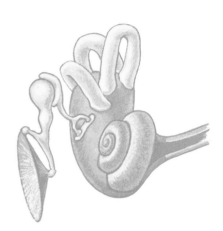

able as to be inevitable. Their importance to the imagination is obvious, now that we are partially liberated from our superiority complex. Many realities may lie beyond the comprehension of human terrestrials, simply because our own outfitting with sense organs is limited. This concept is looked at seriously in a later chapter.

6. The opening to exploitation of the whole electromagnetic radiation spectrum, which gives us an energy spread of not just one octave (violet to red) but of more than 50 octaves, has widened our knowledge of the minutiae of the atomic underworld and emphasized the richness and cosmic significance of the unseeable.

The foregoing preview of six aids to orientation are all recent outcomes of man's persistent exploration of the universe. Although some of the aids were foreshadowed by earlier discoveries, and others have always been vaguely felt, all have approached full development long after the thinking, writing, and theorizing of the ancient and recent church fathers and after the building of most of the formal philosophical systems.

In summary, the discovery of the vastness of the universe that is open to life, the growing conviction that an appeal to the supernatural is unnecessary for the explanation of the beginning and evolution of living organisms, and the fresh ideas now evolving from other high human enterprise, should be sufficient justification for a reconsideration, from time to time, of man's situation and function in the cosmos.

CHAPTER THREE

On Being Incidental

In view of the foregoing argument, we accept the appropriateness of further inquiry as to what should be the human response to the facts revealed by current scientific research. As a first step in the approach to the central questions about the universe — that is, to the questions "What," "How," and "Why" — we shall consider briefly the formal subject of Cosmography. Among other intentions, Cosmography attempts to solve the most intriguing placement problem in the world — the question of the location of man in the universe of space, atoms, and light. Actually, the end product of our efforts may be no more than an approach to knowledge of man's location in a complex cosmos, not a conclusion. Questions without answers will be a recurrent by-product.

Again we loosely define Cosmography as the field of study that has the same relation to the cosmos that geography has to the earth.* Such a statement requires a prior definition of the cosmos, and this is difficult. We shall see later that cosmos means something more than the physical universe. Nevertheless, even though not sharply defined, Cosmography remains a science — a science with decorations. If at times it sounds a bit like scientific philosophy, or even like a phase of religious teaching, so much the better. It will be no loss for religion and philosophy if they are infiltrated with atoms, stars, and the groping of protozoa. (That word "groping" will bear watching. Protozoa are not the only animal gropers!)

For the time being, at least, we shall keep our explorations of cosmic content and activity on the descriptive level. Although Cosmography as here

*Cosmogony and Cosmology are related words frequently confused with Cosmography, and apparently ambiguous even to the lexicographers; the first, however, generally implies pretensions to knowledge of first origins; the second is commonly defined as a branch of metaphysics.

presented is an elementary science, it carries a considerable intellectual voltage, enough to charge to full capacity the more sophisticated inquirer, enough to shock the casual and uninitiated.

Whatever significance and rank we may later assign to life, it early becomes evident that the study of living things can contribute richly to Cosmography. An outstanding example is the association of chlorophyll with the age and structure of the sun and stars. This strange association ties the complicated chemical operation of photosynthesis with the internal anatomy of stellar bodies. The primitive plants of the Archeozoic era,* the green algae, were operating the photosynthetic apparatus more than 1000 million years ago; and the complex leaves of the late Carboniferous* plants also testify to a sun power that has been essentially constant from then to now. The Paleozoic* leaves testify that 300 million years ago the solar radiation was little, if at all, different from that which we now know. The unhurried evolution of stars (at least of one star, the sun) is thus revealed by the Carboniferous ferns. Slow evolution is indicated, but how is it managed? What can be the source of the solar power that radiates energy into space at the rate of more than 4 million tons a second and yet does not exhaust itself over the millions of years?

The full story is too long for presentation here. We simply report that to energize the ancient algae and the tree ferns of the Paleozoic, as well as modern plants, and to activate the animals (including man) who are parasites on the plants, the sun changes hydrogen into helium and radiation, thus providing abundant energy. Fortunately for us, the radiant energy is issued by a self-regulating power plant. The sun is thermostated.

*The terminology applied to the geological ages is explained in Table II of the following chapter.

The collaboration of the various sciences is shown nicely here. Geochemistry, radiology, stratigraphy, atomic physics, and astronomy combine in providing the clear indication that matter can dissolve into radiation. The fossil plants (and animals) indicate the constancy of the sun's heat and thus, through mathematical physics and astrophysics, reveal much about the internal structure of stars.

In the study of the inanimate universe there are many other tie-ups with biology. In the running of ants we can measure an energy flow that is as closely controlled by temperature as is the outpouring of energy from distant stars. To study thoroughly the early climates of this planet we must bring together the methods and facts from a dozen scientific fields, some of them biological, some of them physical. When we see that many rules of nature apply equally to biological cells and to chemical molecules, and when, as later elaborated, we note the impressive probability of millions of planets with highly developed organisms, we must conclude that the world of life should be admitted as a part of the cosmographic picture.

Cosmography, when ideally described and studied, involves an extensive and complicated content. It is too extensive to be handled thoroughly in brief compass. Cosmography appears to be manageable, however, if used chiefly as an instrument in human orientation. In what follows in this chapter and the next we shall report on an attempt to survey sketchily the material universe, with principal emphasis on the basic entities, and on the extent to which the exploration of them and with them appears to pinpoint terrestrial man in the overall scheme.

Our sense organs are definitely limited in number and power, and our experience in thinking about the cosmos has extended through only a few millennia — scarcely more than a dozen of the revolutions of the outermost planet, Pluto. Too much should not be expected of us. We are tyros in the project of cosmic interpretation. Although our accomplishments appear to be rather substantial when we look into our past, have we not unrolled as yet only a fringe of one page of the total Cosmic Writ?

From where we now stand in knowledge of the world it appears that the basic entities of the material universe are, as stated in Chapter 1, the simple-sounding qualities or entities of *space, time, matter,* and *energy.* Of the four, we note, as mentioned in Chapter 1, that matter and energy are two forms of the same thing, tied together by the most popular mathematical equation of our times (after $2 + 2 = 4$), namely $E = Mc^2$. The equation says simply that to transform mass, M, into energy, E, or energy into mass, we apply the square of that most fundamental of natural units, c, the velocity of light in centimeters per second.

By way of the relativity theory, space and time are now also commonly united as space-time. For our present practical approach, however, we shall ignore these postulates of equivalence, which arrange our entities in two pairs, and treat each entity separately. But first, a few remarks on the simple technologies of human understanding.

The Four Elementary Alphabets

History records that the human cultures of the past few millennia have been based to a large extent on the use of some simple aids to communication. These aids we shall call *alphabets,* widening the meaning of that word because more than the traditional ABC's are involved. Without the alphabets we could not readily ask and answer questions on a high level, or communicate easily from the present to the future. Since their invention or emergence, alphabets have enabled men to coordinate better their knowledge and ideas, and to comprehend many phases of the surrounding world. They have served to reduce the seeming chaos and to lay the foundation for civilized cooperation among individuals and groups. The alphabets have also enabled men to advance their cultures and to build stable societies.

The primitive grunts, squeaks, and gestures that evolving man had brought forth from the ancestral jungles did not long suffice for such a mind-evolving primate. He had no marvelous antennae with which to communicate with his fellows, such as those possessed by the ants and used by them in building up their elaborate societies. Evolving man, if he were to survive and grow as a cosmic interpreter, had to devise and use symbols for social communication, and he had to do so more effectively than did the competing animals and his own jungle ancestors. For useful communication he had to associate the symbols with sounds and ideas. In brief, to build his colonies and eventually his intercolony cultures, it became essential for him to tabulate the symbols and to devise writing, reading, and arithmetic.

It was a few thousand years ago that the elementary alphabets began to appear. They came in the form of the ABC's and the 1, 2, 3's. The letters could be formed into words to represent ideas, and in the various isolated cultures the letters and words became standardized. The words were formed into phrases, the phrases into sentences, and in some of the higher cultures the sentences were assembled into chapters, books, and libraries.

The number alphabet was basic for primitive economics, and, with the ABC's, eventually produced the business operations of the modern world. The numbers led to our systems of weights and measures. Without these alphabets — the letters and numbers — culturally we would be little advanced beyond the birds, bees, and apes.

Two other elementary alphabets have long existed. One is connected with the entity Time and the other with the entity Space. They are, respectively, the calendars of days, weeks, months, and years, and the maps that record space measures on the face of the earth, that is, record the terrestrial latitudes and longitudes which permit the delimitation of fields, cities, and states.

But these elementary alphabets — the letters, numbers, calendars, and maps — no longer suffice, either in the study of Cosmography, or in any general effort to understand a world that has become enormously rich in informational content. They met our needs up to a century or two ago. With the growth in amount of measures, however, it has become necessary to supplement the elementary alphabets and introduce further tabulations. Several well-organized, small, tabular categories have been set up to facilitate the acquiring of knowledge about kinds of stars, species of atoms, plant varieties, rock series, and the like. We shall call these tables minor alphabets.

To assist further in our cosmographic study, it is now proposed to construct a major comprehensive alphabet for each of the four entities: time, space, matter, and energy. Through the use of these tabulations we shall remove many of the natural complexities arising from so much information. Fortunately, two of these basic tabulations are already at hand, perfected, and in professional use. They are the periodic table of the elements for matter and the geological ages scale for time. The former concerns matter in its elemental forms; the latter concerns time in large chunks. We shall begin our discussion, however, with a new table that is specially designed to illustrate our position in space — but first, a digression.

On the Goals of Cosmography

As scientists and dreamers we are curious about our position in the plan of the universe. Curious also about the "planning," and sometimes inclined to talk about The Planner. It is a fascinating enterprise. We can have a stimulating and in the end satisfying experience in contemplating cosmographic facts and in speculating on human fate and fancy.

The position of mankind is, of course, an absorbing subject, in part because man is an amusing and somewhat vain animal, but more because he is, whether he knows it or not, aimed at the stars. However ruthless he may have been in his jungle childhood and during his non-social past, he is now instinctively ethical, not so much because virtue may please his tribal gods, but because ethical principles are good economic and social policy. He is also bent on comprehension. Moreover, to make an anticipatory statement, man now knows that he is participating, at a high and complex level, in a great evolutionary drive; he is going along, for the most part cheerfully, with such companions as the vibrating atoms, the radiating stars, the condensing nebulae, the groping protozoa, and the perennial forests with their aspiring birds and butterflies.

As cosmographers we enjoy the decipherment of some of the rules of the cosmic evolution game. We salute the biological winners when we recognize them, such as some of the crinoids and the club mosses whose ancestry of unchanged forms can be traced through many geological periods; and we can try to understand the losers, such as the trilobites of the early Paleozoic, the dinosaurs of 100 million years ago, and Neanderthal Man. We occasionally venture to the borders of science to seek deep answers and to discuss our hope of contributing to future ages something more than our fragmented skulls in the fossiliferous rock. Naturally we are proud of the varied beauty of human thought and contrivance, proud of our poetry and song. We are actors in a great cosmic play where the performers include the atoms, the galaxies, and the eternal intangibles.

The prophets of ancient Israel gloried at times in the magnificence of the universe, which in their time was, of course, centered on man. Those

days of prophecy, however, were for man very early — chronologically more than a third of the way back to the beginning of human cultures. What the inquiring mind has since uncovered would have been totally incredible if revealed to the ancient prophets. Their vision was, we now see, myopic. Our vision is doubtless also deficient, but at least we recognize that we are taking part in a play far grander than that foretold in ancient times. The advance notices of two or three millennia ago greatly undervalued these later chapters in the flowing cosmic drama. Reverence then had to be supported by imaginings and superstitions.

But the accepted facts of now far transcend the fictions of not so long ago. That is how it seems, at any rate, to those who look downward into atoms and the biological cell and upward to the stars. To be reverent, we now have no need of superstitional aid.

In our cosmological inquiries we may appear boastful when speaking of the inadequacies of the ancient philosophies; but we always suffer a healthy pride-shrinking experience when we foresee that a century from now we of the 1960's may be considered to have been primitives in knowledge and thought. We hope such progress will be the lot of mankind. Indeed, two of the present goals in the exploration among galaxies and atoms are the same goals that should and do prevail in all fields of science, namely, to strengthen the evidence on which we can construct our current understandings and to contribute through research to the rapid obsolescence of our presently cherished hypotheses. We hope for greater knowledge and sounder ideas in the future. Deeper thoughts will surely come, a wider spread of the senses, a fuller appreciation of the functioning of the human brain, higher ambitions for men participating in the greatest operation of nature — an operation of cosmic dimensions that might simply be called Growth.

With this glimpse of the welcome challenge, we now return to the basic alphabets of Cosmography — return to what we now recognize as the Tables of Higher Orientation.

CHAPTER FOUR

Packages of Information

We begin the consideration of organizations in nature with a look at the varied types of *human* associations, thus flattering an animal group that will have few firsts. The simplest human organization is the family. Maintaining most of their individualities, families are naturally grouped into neighborhoods or villages. But villages and neighborhoods of men rarely remain entirely independent of each other; they form states and nations, and the individual becomes less autonomous and less free as the higher grouping develops. Beyond the category of nation we may have eventually on this planet a world state, or at least a world-wide cooperating human civilization.

A further step in societal organization, beyond the human family and the associations of families and groups, is the integrated society, so named by A. N. Toynbee. It has appeared among the protozoa Volvox at low levels of assembly and social coordination, and most conspicuously among the social insects (bees, wasps, ants, and termites) at the highest level attained in the animal kingdom.

Wherever we find organization we can assume the existence of an organizing force or cause. In the human family the binding force is love, broadly said; and for our higher associations, village, state, and nation, it is principally security that encourages societal development, but also cultural ambitions and the desire for an abundant economic life. With the social insects the binding attractions are complicated and not fully understood, but the taste organs are doubtless involved, and among the ants the thrills of the interchange of swallowed food.

Spatial Dimensions — An Alphabet for Organizations in Nature

In the microcosmic *inanimate* world the organizational tendencies are governed by electrostatic and other similar forces. The fundamental particles (electrons, neutrons, etc.) organize first into atoms, and the atoms into molecules and molecular systems, and on in complexity to larger organizations in the crystals and colloids.

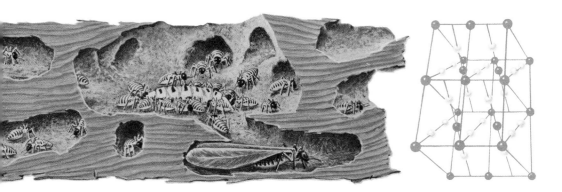

With each higher organization, as with human society, the elemental freedoms are increasingly cramped. The wild liberties of an atom in the vacuum of intergalactic space have been largely lost to the air molecules of oxygen and nitrogen in a closed test tube, where the incessant collisions prevent any one molecule from getting anywhere. The atomic operations in the solid metals of my pencil are so much further cramped, confined, and controlled that I do have a pencil — composed of agitated electrons, protons, and neutrons that cannot freely escape into the interplanetary spaces. For the advantages of organization, the price is the loss of elemental freedoms. A civilization, for example, loses much in individual liberties, since excesses in freedom would lead to deficits both in security and in social advantage. The freely roaming and unpoliced dinosaurs, I like to remember, had no plumbing!

As we proceed to greater and more massive organizations, we begin to leave the microcosmos at the colloidal level. We enter the macrocosmic world where gravitation appears as the effective control. In the sidereal realm we find dust particles gravitating into protostars, with gas pressure and radiation opposing the dominating gravitation. Planets with satellites carry on the organizational theme. Stars frequently appear in pairs and triples. Star clusters and clouds of stars are next in magnitude, and these, with the scattered single and multiple stars, are congregated into the great cosmic units called galaxies. A continuous sequence, we find, from atoms to the Metagalaxy (Table I).

The ever higher organizing of organizations thus appears to be a basic tendency of nature, and making use of this property we can construct an important alphabet — a table to define our own place in the entity Space.

The system of material organizations is displayed in Table I. Everything material is included, even the undiscovered fundamental particles and the transcendent superorganizations. The major subdivisions are shown for all classes.

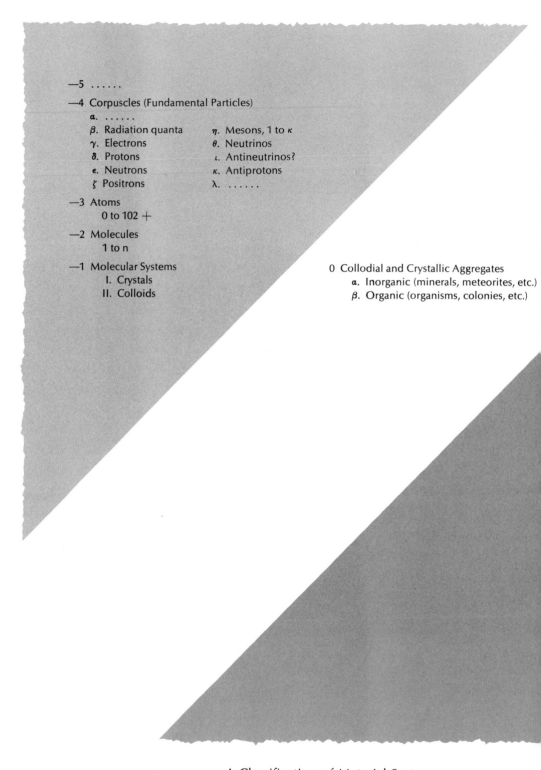

—5 . . . . . .
—4 Corpuscles (Fundamental Particles)
   α. . . . . . .
   β. Radiation quanta   η. Mesons, 1 to κ
   γ. Electrons   θ. Neutrinos
   δ. Protons   ι. Antineutrinos?
   ε. Neutrons   κ. Antiprotons
   ζ Positrons   λ. . . . . . .
—3 Atoms
   0 to 102 +
—2 Molecules
   1 to n
—1 Molecular Systems
   I. Crystals
   II. Colloids

0 Collodial and Crystallic Aggregates
   α. Inorganic (minerals, meteorites, etc.)
   β. Organic (organisms, colonies, etc.)

TABLE I   A Classification of Material Systems

22

+5 Galaxies
    A. Bright
        I. Irregular (I)
        II. Spiral (S)
            α. Abnormal (Sp)
            β. Barred (SB)
                (I) Open (SBc)
                (II) Medium (SBb)
                (III) Concentrated (SBa)
            γ. Regular (S)
                (I) Arms Very Wide (Sd)
                (II) Arms Wide (Sc)
                (III) Arms Close (Sb)
                (IV) Arms Very Close (Sa)
        III. Spheroidal (E)
            a. Most Elongated (E7)
            b. Less Elongated (E6)
            . . . .
            g. Least Elongated (E1)
            h. Circular Outline (E0)
    B. Faint (Bruce classification)
       Concentration and Shape
       a1 a2 a3 . . . . a10
       b1 b2 b3 . . . . b10
       . . . .
       f1 f2 f3 . . . . f10

+6 Galaxy Aggregations
    1. Doubles
    2. Groups
    3. Clusters
    4. Clouds
    [5. Field Irregularities]

+7 The Metagalaxy
    α. Organized Sidereal Bodies and Systems
       1. Meteors   4. Stars
       2. Satellites 5. Clusters
       3. Planets   6. Galaxies
    β. The Cosmoplasma or Matrix
       (α.) Interstellar Particles
          1. Cosmic Dust and Meteors
          2. Diffused Nebulosity (dark)
       (β.) Interstellar Gas
          1. Corpuscles
          2. Atoms
          3. Molecules
       (γ.) Radiation
       (δ.) . . . .

+8 The Universe: Space-Time Complex

+9 . . . .

+1 Meteoritic Associations
    1. Meteor Streams
    2. Comets
    3. Coherent Nebulosities

+2 Satellitic Systems
    I. Earth-Moon Type
    II. Jovian Type
    II. Saturnian Type

+3 Stars and Star Families
    α. Stars with Secondaries
       I. With Coronae, Meteors, and Comets
       II. With Nebulous Envelopes
       III. With Planets and Satellites
    β. Stars with Equals
       I. Close Pairs (or Multiples)
          a. Eclipsing
          b. Spectroscopic
       II. Wide Pairs (or Multiples)
          (α) Gravitational
          [(β) Optical]
       III. Motion Affiliates

+4 Stellar Clusters
    α. Open
       [a. Field Irregularities]
       b. Associations
       c. Loose Groups
       d. Compact Groups
       e. Dense Groups
    β. Globular
       I. Most Concentrated
       II. . . . . . .
       . . . . . .
       XII. Least Concentrated

Subdivision symbols:

α, β, γ . . . . differences largely dependent on basic nature
0, 1, 2, 3 . . . . differences largely dependent on size or mass
I, II, III . . . . differences largely dependent on structure
A, B, a, b . . . . differences largely dependent on position of observer

The three groups in square brackets are chance associations, not gravitational systems.

The entry, −3, *Atoms*, appears later as Table III subdivided in detail: it is the alphabet of matter, with its hundred different atomic species.

Such a listing of organizations, arranged in order of increasing average dimensions, provides the framework for ideas concerning the compulsions and attractions involved when individuals, whether physical or biological, form groups.

The subdividing of some of the numbered organizations would be extensive and instructive, for instance, the subdividing of the biological groupings that here appear only parenthetically in Subclass β of Class 0. In our table of cosmic organizations we can allow little space for organisms if we are to preserve a fair balance. There is too much known for tabling all biological forms. A full display of the ancestry of man would run in decreasing inclusiveness through ten categories, each of which would require further subdividing:

Terrestrial Animate Nature (plants, animals, protista)

KINGDOM:	Animal
PHYLUM:	Chordata (one of about 15 phyla in the animal kingdom)
SUBPHYLUM:	Vertebrata
CLASS:	Mammalia
ORDER:	Primates
FAMILY:	Hominidae (we are here drawing away from the apes)
GENUS:	Homo
SPECIES:	Sapiens
VARIETY OR RACE:	Caucasian
INDIVIDUALS	

and there are various intermediate categories, such as subclass and super-family.

The negatively numbered groups in the table of material systems are in the part of the sequence we call the Microcosmos; the positively numbered are Macrocosmic. Electrostatic and molecular forces, as noted above, govern the organization in the Microcosmos, gravitation in the Macrocosmos. Counteracting the molecular and the gravitational attractions are the dispersing forces: radiation, gas pressure, electrostatic repulsion, and "cosmic repulsion." This last is the name we give to the somewhat vague operator that forces the superorganization of galaxies to disperse except in regions of clustered galaxies where gravitation still weakly controls the situation.

We might question the propriety of entering −4, *Fundamental Particles,* in a listing of material systems. Are these corpuscles actual organizations or are they indivisible units? They are listed here as organizations in anticipation of the submicroscopic analyses in the future which may clearly reveal the structure of electrons and protons. Neutrons, in a sense, are

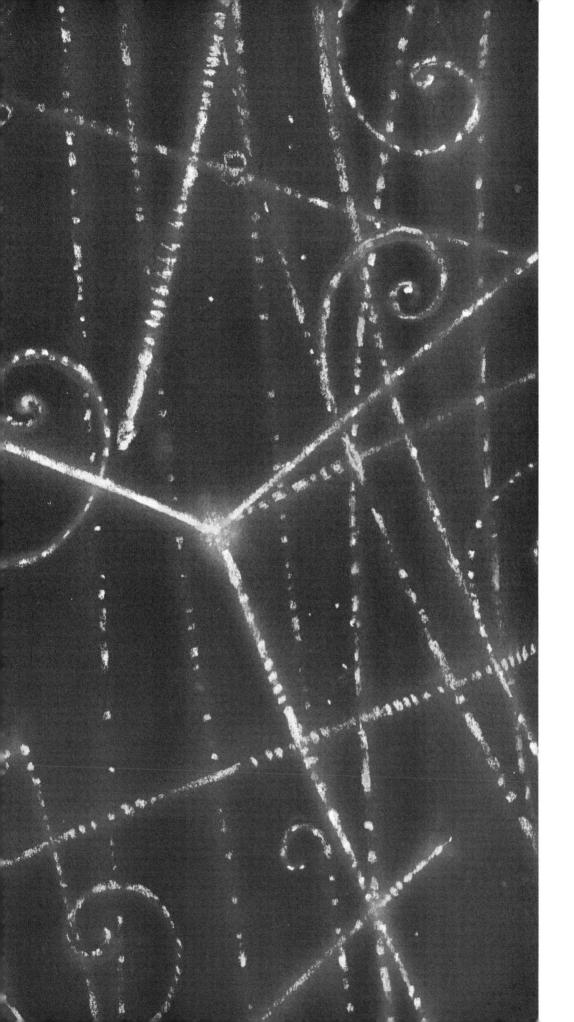

The cloud chamber
makes visible
the tracks of
atomic particles.

already recognized as composite. In any case, the fundamental particles should be included in the table so that we may have here a complete listing of the known material structures.

Classes −5 and +9, now empty in Table I, are challenges to the future. There is so much curiosity and ingenuity within the parentheses of Class 0, Subclass β, that it would be unwise to close the doors, at either end of the series, to the possibility of future revelations. We also leave openings to accommodate further discovery among the Fundamental Particles, and likewise in the contents of interstellar space. As to the former, we are by this challenge asking if there may not be something more fundamental than radiation quanta, or if there may not be other fundamental particles not included in our generous listing. As to the latter, in the fourth part of the Cosmoplasma or Matrix, we are inquiring if there may not be something specific and measurable in interstellar space besides dust particles, gases, and radiation. (Space quanta? Instons of time? Emergons? Psychons?) A generation ago we considered atoms to be made up of electrons and protons only. Now look at the listing of fundamental particles. The category Mesons, with which I associate the V-particles, includes now a score of evanescent but nevertheless fundamental structural units.

Geological Ages — A Higher Alphabet for Time

Looking again at our listing of material systems, which extend from subelectrons to the space-time complex and beyond, we are impressed by the fact that motion prevails throughout the long series. Everything is moving. The movements are relative to various zero points or coordinate systems. The radiation quantum represents an energy transfer in space with the speed of light, and the electrons in the atom also move at tremendous speeds, according to commonly accepted atomic models. But such high velocities are not usual. Some of the relative motions, like those of crystals fixed in rock, differ immeasurably from zero. Other slow motions are those of animals on a planetary surface. Intermediate speeds include the velocity of a comet in passage around a star, and the recession of nearby galaxies in an expanding universe.

Notwithstanding its universality, motion is not a fundamental or basic entity of the material universe. It represents a change of position, and the speed of a change is measured as space (length) divided by time: $v = s/t$. The prevalence of motion everywhere emphasizes, therefore, that time is a basic factor in the career of material systems. Growth and decay are time-linked. Organizations can originate and fade away. For example, comets dissolve; open star clusters revolving around the galactic nucleus are slowly dismembered by gravitation-incited shearing; molecules are forced by temperature to dissociate; organic bodies rot; and nations decay. The time element everywhere enters the panorama of the universe. We can aid our understanding of origins and growth, of decay and death, by an *alphabetization of time* intervals, much as our space concepts are aided by the table of material systems.

For the full discussion of operations that involve temporal sequences, we need a very comprehensive calendar. In fact, we need many kinds of clocks and calendars, tuned to the many various needs. Those that now hang conveniently in the office and home are of no use in timing the laboratory's transmutation of hydrogen atoms into helium, or the explosive release of the atomic energy that runs the stars. Nor, on the other hand, are such calendars useful in measuring the relatively slow evolution of beetles or the rotation of a galaxy. The intervals are too coarse for electrons, too fine for mountain building. For the latter, however, a most impressive calendar is at hand — the geological ages table.

One of the most fortunate evolutionary breaks that has come to inquiring mankind, supplementary to the provision of his relatively large cerebral cortex, is his having evolved on the surface of a planet that is extremely old. Probably the first life forms, and certainly the oldest rocks of the earth's crust, were already in existence in the very early days of our expanding universe. When the trilobites dominated the shallow seas, the galaxies were

much closer together than in present years. Many of our brightest stars, it is now believed, were born long after the great Mesozoic lizards (dinosaurs) disappeared. We can, if we will, use our geological calendar astronomically and speak of Pliocene stars and Cretaceous galaxies.

Since prehistoric times the rotation of the earth in the vacuum of surrounding space has been accepted as our best time-keeper. The earth's rotation was and is measured against the distant stars which are used as fixed reference points, and its period, the day, is known with astounding accuracy — to a millionth of a second. But that is not good enough for modern science. The earth's rotation is slightly disturbed by the variable distribution each year of polar snow and ice, and there are internal adjustments of the

rock layers beneath the surface of the earth which can also affect its regularity. Moreover, the moon, through its production of tides in the earth's air, water, and land, acts as a brake on the rotation; the sun does the same, but less effectively because more distant.

The earth's incompetence as a keeper of the most highly accurate time has incited the development of ingenious time-keepers, such as those involving the very precise pendulum slave-clocks, and the vibration of crystals and of the atoms inside the molecules of ammonia. Other atomic time-pieces are currently under development.

The pulsating variable stars are also celestial time-keepers but, in practice, of low accuracy, as are the circling satellites of Jupiter and Saturn. The revolving of our sun and the naked-eye stars around the center of the galaxy provides a time unit of some 200 million years, with an uncertainty, however, not in seconds, days, or months, but in the millions of years. This big time unit, the cosmic year, even though only roughly known, is of interest when we consider the transformation of galaxies from one type to another. It enters into predictions of the time necessary to dissolve the Pleiades, and in speculations on the age of our Milky Way.

The most impressive and useful calendar for Cosmography, however, is that provided by the spontaneous and natural decay of uranium, thorium, and other radioactive elements that are embedded in the rocks of the earth's crust. Paradoxically, the micro-microseconds of the radioactive atomic transformations are involved in the construction of the geological calendar for which the millennia are the time units. We use the briefest to measure the longest.

As with the timing of a galactic explosion, the percentage accuracy for geological dating is not high. Nevertheless, this Calendar of the Eras is one of the prize threads of information that man has laboriously unraveled.

TABLE II

Geological Time Table

ERA and Period	Time in 10^6 years since beginning of Period	Representative and Dominant Organisms
PSYCHOZOIC		
Pleistocene	1	Primates, Insects, Flowers, Fishes, Birds
CENOZOIC		
Pliocene	15	
Miocene	35	Mammals, Grasses, Birds, Insects, and
Oligocene	50	Flowering Plants; Turtles, Fishes, Snakes,
Eocene	60	and Crocodiles
Paleocene	70	
MESOZOIC		
Cretaceous	120	First Birds, Mammals, Flowers, and De-
Jurassic	170	ciduous Trees; Dinosaurs, Fishes, Cycads,
Triassic	200	Insects, Ammonites
PALEOZOIC		
Permian	220	
Pennsylvanian	240	Fishes, Ferns, Frogs, Corals, Crinoids, Early Conifers, First Insects
Mississipian	260	
Devonian	310	
Silurian	350	Algae, Corals, Starfish, Crinoids, First
Ordovician	400	Ferns, First Fishes, Clams, Snails, and
Cambrian	500	Trilobites
PROTEROZOIC	(1,000)	Algae and First Sponges
ARCHEOZOIC	(2,000)	First Algae
COSMIC	(5,000)	Preorganic

Associated with the radioactive rocks, where the automatically decaying atoms of uranium grow fewer with time while the end products, helium and lead, grow more numerous, we find the fossils of ancient life. We find bones, sometimes, and shells, leaf traces, seeds, and tracks in the ancient fossilized sands and mud. We properly assume that the age of the rocks, which radioactivity measures, is also the age of the fossils. From their own standpoint the animals and plants of past eras are very dead, but they are exceedingly alive in our reconstruction of the story and tempo of biological evolution. The distribution, nature, and age of these fossils also assist in solving the puzzles of the origin of our planet and the secrets of its early days. Again we note that some of the fossil plants in the rocks testify dramatically to the long dependability of sunlight as we know it.

The geological time table has been worked out by investigators in geology, radiology, paleontology, geophysics, and geochemistry. It provides a fairly good calendar back to the beginning of the Cambrian era, 500 million years ago (Table II). It also roughly dates the much older igneous rocks that are associated with the most ancient dim records of simple algae and fungi. These records are scanty and not too sure, but they suggest an age of at least 2000 million years for organisms that knew how to use sunlight for energy.

Although uranium, thorium, radium, and lead were the principal elements originally involved in the construction of the radioactivity-based geological calendar, several other chemical elements are now used in the dating of fossils, rocks, and human artifacts. Among them are potassium decaying into calcium and argon, rubidium into strontium, and the relative abundance of isotopes of oxygen and carbon. Probably additional elements will become useful as techniques improve. The time table has increasing dependability.

The geological eras and periods, with the times of their beginnings, and a reference to their biology, are presented in Table II without subdivision and without further comment at this point on the significance of rock ages in Cosmography.

The Periodic Table of the Species of Atoms

The third of our four tables is probably the most compact and meaningful compilation of knowledge that man has yet devised. The periodic table of the chemical elements does for matter what the geological ages table does for cosmic time. Its history is the story of man's great conquests in the microcosmos. Following the pioneer work of Newlands, Mayer, and especially Mendeléev, an inspired band of workers in chemistry and physics has brought to essential completeness this basic categorizing of atoms.

The tabulation displays all the species of atoms arranged in vertical *groups* and horizontal *series,* and, when given fully, supplies much information about atomic structure. (The symbols are abbreviations of the names of the elements, which are listed in all modern elementary text books.) The table encompasses all kinds of matter, from hydrogen (atomic number 1) through helium, carbon, oxygen, iron, silver, gold, uranium (atomic number 92), up to the several unstable elements heavier than uranium which are creations of our atomic power houses. The last five are named for Einstein, Fermi, Mendeléev, Nobel, and Lawrence.

The scientists of the past century have not only constructed this complete two-dimensional coherent alphabet of matter, but, through the production and identification of scores of *isotopes,* they have produced for the table a third dimension. Thanks chiefly to the transmuting powers of the modern atom-smashers, all the kinds of atoms can be made to appear in isotopic form, that is, with variously weighted nuclei. For example, the naturally radioactive uranium atom may weigh either 238 or 235 units (hydrogen, 1 unit). Mercury has ten isotopes, seven of them stable. Tin has ten stable and seven radioactive isotopes. Many isotopes occur naturally; still more are only man-made.

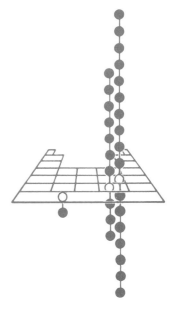

Although the atomic weights differ for the various isotopes of an element, its outer structure of electrons, and therefore its chemical and spectroscopic properties, are essentially identical from one isotope to another.

For most of the elements the artificial isotopes, made in the cyclotrons, are short-lived, vanishing through radioactive decay in small fractions of a second. The dangerous by-product of the hydrogen bomb, strontium 90, is, alas, not an evanescent isotope; for scores of years after its explosive creation it remains a poisonous menace.

The radioactive isotopes of many common elements underlie the tracer techniques that are now so potent in medical diagnosis and therapy, and in biological research. They are also increasingly important in geology. Using an analogy, we may say that the tracer elements, radium, lead, rubidium, etc., provide a diagnosis of the aging of rocks and therefore, by way of fossil plants, provide a chart of the past vitality of the sun.

Without the principles and practical knowledge underlying the groups and series of the periodic table, the modern industrial age would not have been possible. And on the "impractical" side, no tabulation could better illustrate the value of the higher alphabets for the orientation of mankind in the material universe.

TABLE III

Periodic Table of Elements

1 H									2 He
3 4 5 6 Li Be B C									7 8 9 10 N O F Ne
11 12 13 14 Na Mg Al Si									15 16 17 18 P S Cl Ar
19 20 21 22 K Ca Sc Ti	23 24 25 V Cr Mn		26 27 28 Fe Co Ni		29 30 31 32 Cu Zn Ga Ge		33 34 35 36 As Se Br Kr		
37 38 39 40 Rb Sr Y Zr	41 42 43 Nb Mo Tc		44 45 46 Ru Rh Pd		47 48 49 50 Ag Cd In Sn		51 52 53 54 Sb Te I Xe		
55 56 57:72 Cs Ba La:Hf	73 74 75 Ta W Re		76 77 78 Os Ir Pt		79 80 81 82 Au Hg Tl Pb		83 84 85 86 Bi Po At Rn		
87 88 89 90 Fr Ra Ac Th	91 92 93 Pa U Np		94 95 96 Pu Am Cm		97 98 99 100 Bk Cf Ei Fm		101 102 103 . . . M No Lw . . .		

*The symbols are abbreviations of the names of the elements, which are listed in all modern chemistry text books.

The student of cosmic chemistry should be familiar with the bright stars and their spectra for a number of reasons. The stars have influenced the philosophical thought of man from the earliest civilizations. They are at the beginning of man's lesson on his place in the universe. Also, they are high-temperature laboratories in which to test not only the properties of atoms, but also the skill of the spectroscopic scientist.

More than 60 of the 90 kinds of atoms known on the earth's surface also register in the solar spectrum. (The spectra of stars are equally revealing.) Doubtless the 30 other elements are in the sun and stars but are not easily detected. Many of the man-made isotopes, however, are terrestrial only or, if in the sun, are not near the solar surface.

We have as yet no evidence of strange chemistries in the stellar laboratories scattered throughout space. The calcium and hydrogen atoms in the most remote of the receding galaxies appear to react as they do at the sun's surface and in the laboratories of terrestrial investigators. Even man-made technetium, number 43 of the periodic table, is now identified in the spectra of some peculiar faint stars. Since technetium is radioactive with a relatively short life, it must be currently manufactured by some as yet undisclosed process near the stellar surface — perhaps in "star spots."

Throughout the accessible universe there appears to be a common chemical composition, though relative abundances differ from star to star.

The World-wide Argon Traffic

The helium, neon, argon, and other inert gases that line up in the last column of the periodic table are minutely present in our atmosphere. With one possible exception (xenon tetrafluoride) their atoms remain free of entangling alliances, unlike the atoms of oxygen and nitrogen which form combinations with many elements and particularly with the carbon on which life is built. Except for argon, these so-called noble inert gases appear only as traces in our atmosphere — altogether scarcely one-thousandth of 1 percent of the earth's air.

In our atmosphere, on the other hand, the atoms of argon are about one-half of 1 percent of the whole population of atoms. They are thoroughly mixed with the oxygen and nitrogen, and become a median of exchange between all air-breathers of the past, present, and future. They neither perish nor yield their individualities to molecular combinations. They do not escape into interplanetary space as do the lighter, swifter atoms of hydrogen and helium. They originate as one product of the natural radioactivity of one of the isotopes of potassium — potassium 40.

With each breath that we or any other man-sized animal breathes, 40,000 million billion argon atoms are inhaled; and then, without loss, since they do not combine with anything, they are exhaled for rapid and thorough diffusion by the winds throughout the earth's atmosphere. Some of the argon atoms breathed in his first day by Adam (or any early man) are in the next breath of all of us. Some of the argon of our breathing today will be in the first breath of all human infants a century hence. The infant's first breath will also include thousands of argon atoms that the last of the dinosaurs used in his perishing gasp. This argon traffic is obviously rich in suggestion: it implies a droll one-worldness and, like sunshine, it recognizes no national boundaries. It links us in a communal way with the air-breathing animals of the remote past and the distant future.

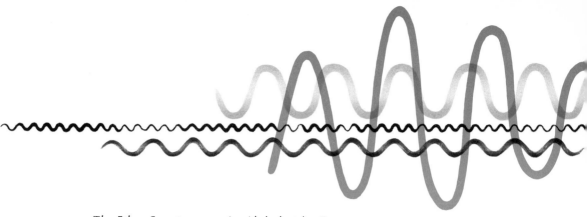

The Ether Spectrum — An Alphabet for Energy

A table that simplifies the consideration of energy will complete the collection of major cosmographic aids. Such a tabulation is derivable from the so-called ether spectrum, or electromagnetic spectrum of radiation. It is not as comprehensive and satisfactory as are the tables available for space, time, and matter. There are energies, gravitational and mechanical, that are not directly included in the radiation sequence. But for exploring and understanding the total universe, the most revealing energies are those recorded in the electromagnetic spectrum. It was such radiant energy that made possible the origin of terrestrial life and its continuation. Our existence, our warmth, our food, and most of our knowledge now depend on the solar energy transmitted through a short segment of the ether spectrum. (Atavismic sun worship, by the way, should be natural religion for thoughtful humans.)

Omitting the subdivisions, we can exhibit this tabulation in brief and simple form (Table IV). We should note, with high respect for his intellect and industry, that man himself, with artificial sense organs, has extended the recognizable spectrum sequence far beyond that known throughout all human history until a century ago. His knowledge and use of radiant energy is no longer confined to the small violet-to-red segment. It ranges beyond the violet through ultraviolet and x-radiation to gamma rays. In the other direction it goes beyond the red and infrared to radio, and to the macro-waves of the light and power services of home and industry. His "supplementary sense organs" that permit these extensions include photographic emulsions, thermocouples, photon tubes, transistors, oscilloscopes, Geiger counters, cloud chambers, and a maze of other electronic gadgetry. Pretty good for a recently emerged primate!

A full discussion of energy as a fundamental entity would include many recent scientific developments of relevance to Cosmography. It would detail the steps taken by physicists, astronomers, and engineers in extending spectrum analysis down into the short-wave, high-energy radiations. It would report how man's visual organs, the eyes, have been gradually supplemented by the ingenious accessories noted above. Nature's simple provision has been far transcended.

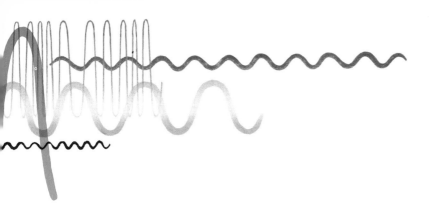

TABLE IV

The Radiation Sequence

Cosmic rays, Primary	(—20)	Visual light	(—6.4 to —6.2)
Secondary	(—15)	Infrared	(—6.2 to —4)
Gamma radiation	(—12)	Microwaves	(—3 to +1)
X-rays, Diagnostic	(—10)	Radio	(+1 to +4)
Soft	(—8)	Power, Light	(+7)
Ultraviolet, Hard	(—7)	Macrowaves	(+8 . . .)
Soft	(—6.5)		

(Representative wave lengths in meters, expressed as powers of 10; see page 9.)

A score of hitherto untouchable octaves of the electromagnetic spectrum, both short waves and long, have been explored. X-rays were discovered about 70 years ago and promptly put to use to advance human health and human knowledge. The invisible ultraviolet has become a tool of industry and of medicine, and an aid to research into the nature of molecules and of biological cells. Equally great human service and industrial development has resulted from the extension of that original one octave of visual light into the realm of the longer waves.

The explosive energies of the gamma rays in the ultra-short wave lengths have created a new culture — the atomic civilization. In a few short decades the explorations of the entities Energy and Matter have changed the way of human life and have deeply affected man's social philosophy.

It is one thesis of this essay that these scientific discoveries, and the technology built upon them, may have forced the older philosophies and creeds to substantial readjustment; they point to the possibility of radical modification of some of the basic tenets. This idea is elaborated indirectly in later chapters.

The radiation spectrum is involved in many other outstanding developments such as: (1) the penetration of the ozone layer in the earth's atmosphere by the war-inspired rockets; (2) the modern alchemy of transforming one atom into another through bombardment with high-energy photons and high-speed electrons, protons, neutrons, and other corpuscles;

and (3) the fission of heavy atoms and the fusion of lighter ones in the interest of providing atomic energy for beneficent peace and maleficent war.

Some of these items we must later sort out from the abundance provided by the electromagnetic spectrum and examine them in the interest of present interpretations in Cosmography, and for future predictions. They should help in the placement-of-man problem.

Lesser Tables for Cosmography

The four major tabulations can advantageously be supplemented by a few other summarizing aids. Some of them are embodied in the subdivisions of the major tables — for example, the types of galaxies and the kinds of atoms. Five relatively small, useful tabulations are the following:

1. *The planets of the solar system,* their years, days, sizes, distances — all of which are significant in the consideration of the origin of the earth.

2. *The major phyla of animals and plants;* all of these are the terrestrial descendents of sunshine and the primeval "thin soup" of the shallow seas.

3. *Classes of Mammalia,* from whales to bats to cows and the anthropoids.

4. *The sequence of stellar spectra,* a color and temperature progression from bluish hot Rigel in Orion to yellowish Canopus and the sun, and down the temperature scale to reddish Antares and Betelgeuse.

5. *Animal societies,* a series from the salmon with her million eggs, to the monogamous robin, to the buffalo herd and human society, and on to the social integration achieved by honey-bees and fungus-growing ants, which appears to be the ultimate in social organization.

Summary of Orientations in Space, Time, Matter, and Energy

In concluding our review of the placement problem, let us see just where we stand with respect to the basic entities. We are dealing, of course, only with the material universe. I do not see how we can locate ourselves in what might be called the "stream of thought," or find our place in some mystical spiritual category. We shall therefore summarize only in terms of our spot in time, space, and matter.

1. *Time.* In time we are precisely between the past and the future. Concerning the future we can extrapolate a little, but cautiously. As far as

planets, stars, and galaxies are concerned, we see clearly no end to the material universe; we can only guess the future on the authority of incomplete theories. Concerning the past, the indications are clearer that somewhere between 5 and 15 billion years ago there was an epoch, T_0, of extraordinary significance in the history of our physical world. We believe there may have been a specifiable creative moment (or epoch) in the past, but no comparable specifiable moment predicted for the future. We accept tentatively a finity in the past operation of an evolving universe; ahead an infinity.

Unless we deny T_0 and assume that there was no "creation in time," no real beginning of the dust- and star-populated Metagalaxy, no start of the expanding universe, we must conclude that we are relatively young in time. Our days are not near the conclusion of the world, or even midway. The hydrogen fuel that heats the stars is very abundant. We — the galaxies, stars, organisms — are just getting under way. Our 10^{10} past years are brief, negligible of course compared with a future of eternity.

There is, to be sure, an alternative hypothesis. It holds that the explosion of the primeval super-atom that contained everything is illusory, and that the past is "just as infinite" as the future. On this rather tentative hypothesis, which tastes a bit of theology and ancient dogma, there must be a continuous creation (emergence) of matter out of nothing to make up for that which, because of the expansion of the material universe, is lost "over the rim of the world."

The primeval atom theory is the suggestion of Canon Lemaître. It has been much elaborated by George Gamow and his associates. It is certainly consistent with many observations. The "continuous creation" hypothesis is associated chiefly with the names of Jordan, Bondi, Gold, and Hoyle; it has yet to get an observational backing to match its esthetic appeal.

For the present we speculators can safely accept much past duration of time, and as much or more in the future.

2. *Space.* We are more easily located in the size category. It happens that a man is just about as much larger than a hydrogen atom as the sun is larger than a man. Geometrically, as we put it, we are in the middle register in the series of material bodies, that is, $\dfrac{\text{Star}}{\text{Man}} = \dfrac{\text{Man}}{\text{Atom}}$, and this is roughly true whether we are measuring in grams of matter or in centimeters of diameter. Man's location in space among the stars and galaxies is reported in Chapter 8.

3. *Energy.* To place ourselves somewhere in the energy table has practically no meaning. We could compute the amount of energy represented by the masses of our bodies and compare it with the energies represented by the masses of stars and atoms. But that comparison has already been done in effect by finding our place in the organization of material systems. We could locate ourselves in a vague way through indicating the energy that we command, which seems to be tremendous compared with the resources of our forefathers. We now have fuel-fed dynamos; we have hydroelectric plants; and recently we conquered at least a part of atomic energy. But if we add all these terrestrial sources together and claim that they represent our standing in the energy category, they would be as nothing compared with a moment's radiation from an average star. It has been estimated that one substantial earthquake, which is neither man-made nor man-controlled, is energetically equal to 1000 atomic bombs; and energetically speaking, a fair-sized solar prominence makes our "city-busters" dwindle to firecracker dimensions. In short, in the total cosmic operation with energy, man and his works are of minor consequence.

4. *Matter.* By taking a vain and generous view we can claim a much better world position in the category of matter. Negligible and incidental though we may be in space, time, and energy, we do have the distinction of sharing a wide variety of chemical atoms with the greats of the universe — with the planets, stars, galaxies, and cosmic dust. Man is in a sense made of star stuff. Important in his composition are a score of the elements found in the earth's crust. Some of the kinds of atoms are found abundantly in his body; others appear only as traces. The most prominent atoms in the make-up of animal bodies (Mammalia) are the following, with an estimate of approximate percentages:

Oxygen	65%	
Carbon	18	
Hydrogen	10	
Nitrogen	3	
Calcium	2	
Phosphorus	1	
Others	1	

A current theory suggests the following distribution of matter in the atmospheres of the sun and sun-like stars:

Element	Percentage	
Hydrogen	81.73%	▬▬▬▬▬▬▬▬
Helium	18.17	▬▬
Oxygen	0.06	·
Magnesium	0.02	·
Nitrogen	0.01	·
Silicon	0.006	·
Sulphur	0.003	·
Carbon	0.003	·
Iron	0.001	·
Others	0.001	·

And by another interpretation of astrophysical evidence and theory, the sun's composition is this:

Element	Percentage	
Hydrogen	87.0%	▬▬▬▬▬▬▬▬
Helium	12.9	▬▬
Oxygen	0.025	·
Nitrogen	0.02	·
Carbon	0.01	·
Magnesium	0.003	·
Silicon	0.002	·
Iron	0.001	·
Sulphur	0.001	·
Others	0.038	·

Note that hydrogen plus helium in both theories is 99.9 percent of the solar atmosphere.

In the earth's crust, including air and oceans:

Element	Percentage	
Oxygen	49.2%	▬▬▬▬▬▬
Silicon	25.7	▬▬▬▬
Aluminum	7.5	▬
Iron	4.7	▪
Calcium	3.4	▪
Sodium	2.6	▪
Potassium	2.4	▪
Magnesium	1.9	▪
Hydrogen	0.9	ǀ
All others	1.7	▪

But of the earth as a whole, which includes the hypothetical iron-nickel core, we have the following estimate of composition:

Iron	67%	████████████████
Oxygen	12	███
Silicon	7	██
Nickel	4	█
Others	10	███

All of the many human body elements are of course on or in the crust of the earth, and most of them have also been identified in the hot stellar atmospheres. No atomic species is found in animal bodies that is not well known in the inorganic environment. Obviously man is made of ordinary earth and star stuff and should be mighty proud of it.

In one respect the animals and plants excel the stars. In the complexity of their molecules and molecular aggregates, living organisms transcend the atomic combinations of the inanimate world. The sun's hot atmosphere and also the solar interior are found to be relatively simple in chemical structure in comparison with the organic chemistry of a caterpillar. For that reason we are able to understand stars better than we can know the larvae of insects. The stars operate chiefly under the gravitational, gaseous, and radiation laws and are subject to the consequential pressures, densities, and temperatures. The organisms, on the other hand, are hopeless mixtures of gases, liquids, and solids — hopeless, that is, from the standpoint of our working out for them neat and complete mathematical and physico-chemical formulae. The astrophysicist has a simple job compared with the demands upon the biochemist.

CHAPTER FIVE

An Inquiry Concerning Other Worlds

Before we can propose ourselves and our destiny as significant concerns of the universe, we should turn our attention to the probable existence and general spread of protoplasm throughout stellar spaces and cosmic times. We can no longer be content with the hypothesis that living organisms are of this earth only. But before we ponder on the life spread, we should inquire into the prevalence of suitable sites for biological operations. The initial question is not whether such sites are presently inhabited. First we ask: Are there other habitable celestial bodies — bodies that would be hospitable if life were there? No field of inquiry is more fascinating than a search for humanity, or something like humanity, in the mystery-filled happy lands beyond the barriers of interstellar space. But are there such happy lands?

Other Stars, Other Planets, Other Chemistry

It is generally admitted by practical people that we do exist. Extremely few meditators on this subject pretend to a suspicion that we do not exist, that it is all a dream, an illusion, a complicated fancy. Let us go along with the majority and accept your existence and mine, and that of the physical world around us. And to simplify matters, as a preliminary to discussion, let us say that the non-physical world also exists. Around these words "non-physical" and "exists" many battles could be fought, but the weapons would be mostly words, not ideas.

Since we live on an earth where more than a million other kinds of animals are enjoying (or suffering) the same experience in biochemical evolution, we naturally meditate on the nature of this operation called

living. We see a great variety of life forms and extreme diversity in living conditions, and note also the wide adaptability of mankind to varied environments. Naturally we ask: Are the likes of us elsewhere? Are we exactly duplicated? The question is directed sometimes to the pastor or to the philosopher, but usually to the astronomer. On behalf of astronomy I shall venture a reply; but in this chapter we first consider chiefly the antecedent question: Are there planets like ours elsewhere?

Human bodies are constructs of commonly known chemical elements, and nothing else. We have tabulated in the preceding chapter the principal atoms in the bodies of animals, and we must remember that in chemical composition humans are decidedly animal. The element oxygen accounts for about 65 percent of our bodies; 18 percent is carbon, 10 percent is hydrogen, 3 percent nitrogen, 2 percent calcium, and the remaining 2 percent includes silicon, phosphorus, sodium, sulphur, iron, and a dozen other elements — all common to the crust of the earth and to the flames of the sun. The percentages vary somewhat from rat to leech, from watery octopus to crusty coral. There is more than average calcium in the bony vertebrates, more silicon in the brachiopods, more H_2O in the jelly fish; but all animals are composed of the common atoms. The elements uncommon to the rocks, like gold, platinum, and radium, are also uncommon to the bodies of men.

No Life on the Stars

The stars are composed of the same stuff as that which constitutes the sun and the earth's crust. They are built of the same materials as those that compose terrestrial organisms. As far as we can tell, the same physical laws prevail everywhere. The same natural rules apply at the center of the Milky Way, in the remote galaxies, and among the stars and planets of the solar neighborhood.

In view of the common physics and chemistry, should we not also expect to find animals and plants everywhere? That seems completely reasonable; and soon we shall say that it seems inevitable. But to demonstrate the actual presence of organic life in other planetary systems is now impossible for us because the stars are so remote and we, as earth-bound searchers of the sky, are yet too feeble in the face of stellar realities. To

establish through statistical analysis the high probability of planets suitable for living organisms is, however, not difficult. A statistical argument, as a matter of fact, can be more convincing than would be a marginal observation.

It will clarify the discussion if we start with two routine reminders: (1) By life we mean what we terrestrials recognize as life — a biochemical operation involving oxygen, carbon, and nitrogen, and making use of water in a liquid state. (Other kinds are imaginable; e.g., one where silicon replaces carbon, or where sulphur's participation is like that of oxygen, or where liquid ammonia replaces water. Such is imaginable, but unlikely.) (2) Mars and Venus are therefore the only other planets of our solar system that are at all suitable for living organisms.

The evidences are good that Martian life is low and lichen-like, if it exists at all. The surface of Venus was until recently an unsolved problem. Now we know that a blanket effect prevails on Venus and that the surface temperature is much too high for the existence of protoplasm.

Among the many definitions of life is the cold rigid version: "material organizations perpetuating their organization." We might put it better: "the perpetuation by a material organization of its organization." The definition can properly refer both to individuals and to species, and also to societies. They are all at times alive. They all die, if we suitably define death. The lively deathless atoms of our breaths, however, are not, in this defining, alive.

Life is tough, tenacious, and consequently persistent when we give it time to adjust to varying environments. We find it thriving in geysers and hot springs. Some flowers bloom under the snow. Both plants and animals on occasion endure for long periods on hot deserts. Some seeds and spores can withstand desiccation and extreme cold indefinitely. Life as we know it on the earth has wide adaptability; but there are limits, and one of these limits is the heat and radiation near a star's surface, where the molecules constituting protoplasm would be dissociated into atoms.

In our consideration of the spread of life throughout the universe, we must therefore immediately drop all thoughts of living organisms on the trillions of radiant stars. The flames of the sun are rich in the lively atoms of oxygen, carbon, nitrogen, hydrogen, and calcium — the principal constituents of living matter — but physical liveliness and organic livingness are quite different behaviors. At the surfaces of some of the cool stars, like Antares and Betelgeuse, and in the cooling sunspots, we find a few simple molecules in addition to the scores of kinds of atoms; but there is nothing in the stars that is as complicated and tender as the proteins — those molecular aggregates that underlie the simplest life. And of course the stars harbor no water in the liquid state.

No Life on Meteors or Comets

The stars are out of it, therefore, and they probably contain more than half of all the material in the universe. Most of the non-stellar material is believed to be in the form of interstellar gas, with a bit of dust. The dust is of the sort that shows up as meteors, when in collision with the atoms and molecules of the earth's atmosphere; it appears also among the stars as the dark nebulosities that interrupt and make patchy the glow of the Milky Way.

No life exists on these minute meteor specks or on the relatively larger meteorites. It is absent for several reasons. The masses are too small to hold gravitationally an atmosphere. (Even our moon cannot retain the oxygen and carbon dioxide necessary for breathing animals and plants.) Moreover, the meteors out among the stars are too cold for liquid water, and they are unprotected against the lethal untraviolet radiation from hot stars.

How about life on the comets? The same general argument holds as for meteors and meteorites, since the comets are simply assemblages of dusty and fragmented meteoric materials, infused with gases. In addition, most of the large comets of the solar system are when brightest too near the sun for living organisms, and the rest of the time in their orbital travels too frigidly remote in the outer parts of their paths.

Only Planets are Habitable

In our search for life we are therefore left with the planets and those on which it can occur and survive must be neither too near their stars nor so remote from them that the cold is unrelieved. They should not be too small to hold an oxygen atmosphere, unless we are content to settle for primitive anaerobic life. (A few types of low organisms thrive in the absence of elemental oxygen.)

The life-bearing planets must also have non-poisonous atmospheres and salutary waters; but given time enough, organisms could no doubt become adjusted to environments that would be poisonous and impossible for life such as that now developed on the earth.

Finally, the propitious planets that are suitable in size, temperature, and chemistry must also move in orbits of low eccentricity. Highly eccentric orbits would bring their planets too near the star at periastron a part of the year, and then too far out at apastron. The resulting temperature oscillations would be too much for comfort, perhaps even too much for the origin and persistence of early life. Also, in the interest of avoiding too great differences in temperature from night to day, it would be best if the planets rotate rapidly and their rotational axes be highly inclined (as is the earth's) to their orbital planes.

With the foregoing requirements in mind we ask if there are many really suitable planetary systems, and ask also: How are planets born?

Genesis — A Twentieth-Century Version

In the beginning, as they say, was chaos. Or at any rate, soon after the explosive beginning of the expanding universe there was chaos, if we accept the theory of the Primeval Atom as proposed by Canon Lemaître — a theory that visualizes the original assemblage of the matter and energy of the whole universe into one body, into a single super-atom. In those chaotic early times, some 5 to 10 billion years ago, the average density of matter

was of course very high; the stars were near together; many galaxies inter-penetrated, if galaxies existed at that time as organizations, and if not, the evolving proto-galaxies overlapped. Collisions and secondary explosions must have been frequent in those crowded, chaotic times. Masses of flying gas in the cold of space quickly liquefied, solidified, and cooled into planet-like bodies, with a wide range of sizes. Shattering and exploding bodies produced dust grains and gases from which stars were later born.

All that action seems logical, if we accept the hypothesis of a tight little universe before the cosmic expansion spread it out. Let us proceed to sketch in more detail this particular hypothesis relative to the earth's birth. The larger products of the explosive expansion of the super-hot Primeval Atom would remain gaseous. If the masses were not too large or too small they would eventually become luminous stars. Those that were too extended to hold together as single stellar bodies in equilibrium (between the pulling in by gravitational force and the outpushing by radiation pressure and gas diffusion, plus the centrifugal action if the bodies are in rapid rotation) would become double or multiple stars, or clusters of varied populations.

The Lilliputians

The masses that are much smaller than our sun but larger than our planets — and there must be billions of them — provide a mystery, an unexplored element of the stellar universe. Our astronomical records show none of them, but our time is brief on the cosmic clock. They would have mass enough to contract into stable permanent bodies with dense atmospheres, but not mass enough to shine so effectively that they could be recorded, unless very near. The whole range of sizes, from those of 1/50 the solar mass, which we might call dark Lilliputian stars, to those 1/500 the mass of the sun, which we might call Brobdingnagian planets, could be represented by countless sidereal bodies. They may be more numerous than the recognized stars.

The largest of the Lilliputians would shine faintly in infrared light and could be detected if very near, but mostly they are lightless wanderers. Eventually scientific techniques may enable us to detect them. For example, we may detect them through radio signals if such unseen bodies have violently electrical atmospheres or register themselves through excessive volcanic activities. One of them may some day drift into our planetary system, being first revealed by its reflection of sunlight or through perturbations in the motions of our outermost planets or comets. It would be very instructive to encounter some of these intermediate products of an early evolutionary epoch. Their existence can hardly be denied. Their abundance is uncertain, but probably high.

Theories of planetary origin other than the one we are now sketching would also make the Lilliputians' existence highly probable.

Primeval Chaos and the Clean-up

Whether or not there was in the beginning a single primeval "atom" that contained all, there can be little doubt that the now dispersing galaxies with their billions of stars were densely crowded together in the remote past. It is highly significant that the age of the earth's crust, measured by the radioactivity in the rocks, is much the same as the measured age of the expansion.

To go on with the sketch, let us suppose that one particular emerging star (our proto-sun) was densely surrounded with a miscellany of the debris of the original or some subsequent explosion. These cooling secondary bodies would be — at least loosely — in the gravitational control of the star. Among the sun-circling bodies (proto-planets) we further assume that there were one or two so large that they participated effectively in the control of the lesser bodies. If two of these large secondary bodies, which we may name proto-Jupiter and proto-Saturn, were moving in approximately the same plane and same direction around the proto-sun, they would be in a position to govern the motions and dictate the future of the lesser bodies. Some of the small planetary bodies — perhaps most of them — would be moving in orbits too elliptical for safety; they would be either engulfed at perihelion by the sun or by the two giant planets when in the outer parts of their orbits, or perturbed entirely out of the solar system into interstellar space.

In the billions of years that this tripartite mill of the gods has been working, the retrograde bodies, i.e., those circling the sun in the direction opposite to that of the hypothetical large planets, would be disposed of through gravitational perturbations. In fact, the flimsy comets are handled in this fashion in these late days of the mopping up. The directions of their motions are sometimes substantially altered and the eccentricities of their orbits greatly changed. A few are "captured" into smaller orbits. In the long past many must have been ejected forever from the solar system by the larger planets. For when increasing distance from the sun diminishes its gravitational power, a nearby planet can control the destiny of any comet whose orbit brings it near.

According to this hypothesis of Original Chaos and Slow Mopping-up, the proto-planet earth was one of the favored fragments of the catastrophic operation that gave birth to the sun and its accompanying debris. Its orbit was safely circular, or nearly so; its spacing from neighboring planets (Venus, Mars) was such that perturbations were not serious.

At the dramatic time when the solar system was forming, other stars, some of them near the sun, were undergoing a similar experience. It would have been an exciting time for a beholder of the young sky, rich as it then was in comets and meteors and with unseated planets on the loose.

Even if the earth's original orbit and those of the other surviving planets were considerably elongated in the early times, the primitive interplanetary medium of dusty debris, through which the planets circled about the sun, would round off the orbits. This medium of dust would resist the planetary motion; it would tend to lessen the eccentricity of an orbit and thus ensure safety from collision and engulfment. Most of the orbital inclinations (tilts) in the present solar system are similar to those of Jupiter and Saturn — a result, the hypothesis would suggest, of the material impacts and gravitational pulls in the early and long continued times of adjustment from chaos to order.*

The foregoing suggestions as to the origin of the sun's planets, and of other planetary systems around other stars were proposed long ago by the writer in a time of desperation. The two now prevalent theories of planetary origin — nebular contraction and tidal disruption — were at that time in trouble with the observed facts and with the accepted notions about the character and behavior of interstellar dust. "Facts" have been the No. 1 enemy of cosmogonic theories. If we did not know so much, we would have less to explain. The above chaotic origin theory gets around many of the serious difficulties which were confronted by earlier hypotheses that tried to explain all the major regularities in the solar system; but it also has troubles or, rather, insufficiencies. It needs bolstering here and there with protective subhypotheses, as do all the others. The major assumptions back of the chaos theory are the two following:

1. A catastrophic origin of stars (including our sun) some few billion years ago is assumed to have filled space with gaseous, liquid, and solid debris of all sizes; gravitational control over a limited section of space was the natural power of the most massive fragments. In our case the control was vested in the sun.

2. In that primeval aggregation of dust, gas, and planetoidal fragments, dominated by the proto-sun, one or two large proto-planets are

*A better statement would be: "times of adjustment from *apparent* chaos to order," for in this physical world there is no real *chaos;* all is in fact orderly; all is ordered by the physical principles. Chaos is but unperceived order; it is a word indicating the limitations of the human mind and the paucity of observational facts. The words "chaos," "accidental," "chance" "unpredictable," are conveniences behind which we hide our ignorance.

postulated to have circled the all-controlling sun in approximately what is now the mean orbital plane of the solar system.

The rest of the procedure follows naturally — the sweeping-up (or out) of most of the debris and the ordering of the minor pieces into regions and motions of relative safety.

We omit further elaboration of this hypothesis and simply suggest that its insufficiencies include the poor accounting for the remarkable spacing of the surviving planets (this similarly affects other hypotheses), and the almost total absence of high inclinations for the orbits of bodies in the solar system, although long-period comets ignore the common orbital plane and some of the asteroids between Mars and Jupiter still have high inclinations.

A serious thrust at this hypothesis of chaos would be made if we could prove that stars arise through the slow condensation of interstellar nebulosity. Also a protecting subhypothesis, or abandonment, would be necessary if we could assure ourselves that the earth actually was built up gradually over a very long time by the slow accretion of interplanetary matter.

Nevertheless, the hypothesis has the advantage that out of explosions, and what we call chaos, almost any arrangement of materials and motions can be assumed. The present puzzling distribution of orbital and rotational speeds (the angular moment problem) would be irrelevant. As a working hypothesis to show one way in which planetary systems can be formed, the chaos theory is worth preserving, at least until some comprehensive alternative is developed and widely accepted as the only reasonable genesis.

The foregoing hypothesis has been presented in some detail because if such a theory eventually prevails it would carry with it as an important corollary the implication that planetary systems may be just about as common as the stars, that conditions suitable for life permeate the cosmos. And then the questions "Are we alone?" and "Are we a unique biological construct of the universe?" could be answered negatively and emphatically. But there are many other theories of the earth's origin and in the interest of our concern about the distribution of biological habitats we should name those that are more or less convincing.

Many Methods of Planetary Origin

The supernatural deities of various sorts, rather than "accident" or astrophysical operations, were in ancient times given credit for the origin of the earth; but also the assumption that it had always existed was not uncommon. Many of the rationalizations, developed to account for the origin of the inclusive system of sun, planets, satellites, asteroids, comets, and interplanetary dust, are now wholly discredited. Some theories include the origin of the sun; others assume its prior existence before the planets appeared. Most of the theories are of recent date — a natural consequence of, first, the great accumulation of relevant data in the past few years and, second, the increasing population of ingenious speculators. The new knowledge built up by the world's astronomers in the past 40 years is many times greater than that of all time before.

The following list of 15 hypotheses, arranged in approximate chronological order, represents the thoughts of speculative scientists from Israel, Germany, France, Australia, India, America, England, Russia, Sweden, and Holland. This geographical distribution shows the widespread curiosity about man's physical place in the universe.

1. Mosaic cosmogony, and similar early dogmatic statements.

2. Nebular hypothesis, the famous long-enduring Kantian-Laplacian theory.

3. Partial disruption of the sun by an infalling comet, with the production of planets.

4. Solar eruptions providing planet-building "planetesimals."

5. Capture of the planets by the sun from space or from other stars.

6. Tidal disruption of the sun by a passing star, providing gaseous filaments that condense into planets (variant of 4).

7. Glancing collision of stars (variant of 6).

8. Break-up of one component of a binary star by a third passing star.

9. Explosive fission of the hypothetical proto-sun.

10. Disruption of an unstable pulsing variable star (cepheid).

11. Revival of the nebular hypothesis, bolstered by modern theories of dust and gas accretion.

12. Electromagnetically produced condensations in a contracting nebula (variant of 2).

13. Nova explosion in a binary system providing circulating planetoid fragments.

14. Revival of the hypothesis of cold planetesimals operating in a nebulous medium (combination of variants of 4, 11, and 12).

15. Primeval explosive chaos and the Survival of the Conforming — my "hypothesis of desperation" outlined above.

All of these theories could be described in detail. Some of them overlap. A few have been rejected on the basis of obvious failings or because they are not complete hypotheses. For example, Nos. 1, 3, 4, 5, 9, and 10 are out. Nos. 2 and 6 are weak. This leaves Nos. 7, 8, 11, 12, 13, 14, and 15. We should observe that several different methods may be responsible for planetary origins. We do not need to search out one method only to the exclusion of all others.

The general conclusion at this moment must be that not one of the theories is entirely satisfactory. The best of them need further development. Many do not easily account for the following observed regularities and arrangements:

1. The nine major planets revolve in the same direction around the sun.

2. The sun and, so far as known, most of the planets and satellites rotate on their axes in this same direction.

3. The inclinations of the planetary orbital planes are such that the overall system (excluding comets) is exceedingly flat.

4. The smaller planets, except Pluto, which may be an escaped satellite of Neptune, are relatively near the sun; the four greater planets are all from 5 to 30 times the earth's orbital radius from the sun.

5. The satellite systems of Jupiter and Saturn have characteristics simulating those of the planetary system of the sun.

6. Apparently the chemical composition of the earth, probably also of the other planets, is similar to that of the sun, when allowance is made for escaping atmospheres from the surfaces of the smaller planets for which the masses are incapable of retaining the swiftly moving hydrogen, helium, and other light-weight atoms.

7. The distribution of angular momentum in the planetary system appears to be fatal to many of the hypotheses; the sun rotates too slowly, or the planets too fast, to allow for a common origin of sun and planets — unless protective subhypotheses hurry to our assistance.

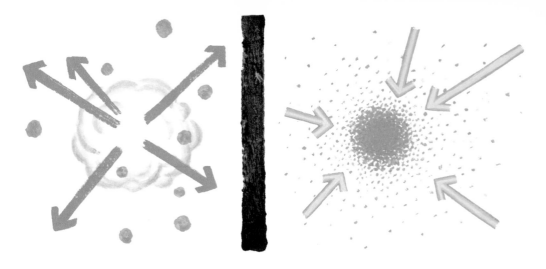

The foregoing theories, with one or two exceptions, can be classified as either catastrophic or as calmly accretional. In other words, the planets were born of violence or of slow building up through the accumulation of material. The former generally visualizes the earth, or at least the proto-earth, as once hot from surface to center. The latter visualizes the earth's surface as never wholly molten, although, as the mass grew from accretion, the center naturally heated up and affected the outer strata.

What do these theories imply with respect to the prevalence of earth-like planets? If the contracting-nebula type of origin of stars is accepted, and the stars are held to result mainly from the condensation of cold clouds of gas and dust with the planets coming along as a by-product, then we must assume that planets like those we know, similar in mass, temperature, and chemistry, are the natural and common product of an evolving universe. The same high frequency would prevail for the Original Chaos and Sweeping-up hypothesis.

We must always remember that our sun is a very ordinary sort of star. One hundred thousand of the brightest million stars are essentially identical with the sun. We detect this similarity by way of spectrum analysis (described briefly in Chapter 7), which tells us of the luminosities, masses, sizes, motions, and chemical compositions of the stars. We get the proportion, 10 percent, from the analysis of large samples. Moreover, stars do not need to be precisely like our sun to have habitable planets. If the star is hotter than the sun, the liquid water zone is farther out; if cooler, the livable planets must be nearer the stellar power plant.

The sun and the aforementioned 100,000 stars like it have no exceptional position in the Milky Way system; they are in the outer part of what appears to be a typical large spiral galaxy in a Metagalaxy where there are millions, perhaps billions, of galaxies of the same spiral type. The sun-like stars (most of them) also have a history dating back to those turbulent, planet-breeding early times. The evidence is increasing, therefore, for an abundance of habitable planets.

There is, however, in all theories of origin one important deterrent to the universal formation and retention of planets with suitable requirements for life. That hindrance lies in the frequent existence of numerous double and multiple stars. A century ago double stars were considered something of a rarity. The picture has changed with the increase of optical power and of skills in discovering binaries and multiples. We now believe that 40 percent or more of the stars are in pairs or triples. Of the 55 stars known to be within 100 trillion miles of the earth, only 31 are single stars, and companions may yet be found for some of them. In a two- or three-star system, planets within the zone of liquid water are highly improbable. The gravitational rules are against it. Orbits would be unstable. We must accept as truly hospitable only single stars, and perhaps very wide double stars where a stable planetary orbit around one of the components might be permitted by the other star. Probably we should also exclude the highly populated centers of globular star clusters.

Infrequency of Collisions

By taking the contracting-nebula hypothesis (say, No. 14), we would be choosing one that is most favorable to the formation and preservation of planets. But suppose we accept instead one of the collisional hypotheses — not the cometary-collision suggestion, since the comets we know about are relatively too small in mass to be potent factors in stellar catastrophes. The collision of two or more ordinary stars would not be very productive of planetary systems because of the infrequency of such collisions. At the present time our sun and its neighbors are so remote from each other that collisions are wellnigh impossible. Twenty-five trillion miles separate the sun from its nearest known stellar neighbor, Alpha Centauri. Any given star, although it be moving at the average relative speed of 20 miles a second, would move around in the galaxy for millions of years without collision or near approach. If we insisted that planetary systems could arise only through the collision or very close approach of mature stars in a fully

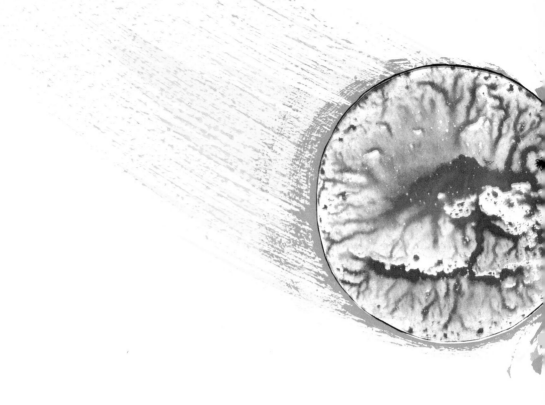

developed galaxy like ours, we would be justified in believing that our own "accident" may have been unique — one birth only in the whole galaxy — and we the offspring of that remote improbable event! We should then answer: "We *are* alone; we are the special care of whatever omnipotence is concerned in caring for rare accidents."

But two observations quickly weaken or defeat that conclusion. The first is that we do not limit our speculations to only this galaxy of 100 billion stellar bodies that are always attracting but avoiding each other; we must consider the increase in the chance of collision that is provided through the circumstance that there are billions of other galaxies within our telescopic reach, and possibly trillions beyond our direct knowing. All of these systems must be considered when we examine the probability of life as a cosmic phenomenon. If only one galaxy in 1000 has had a planet-producing collision among its stars, there would still be millions of such collisions.

The other and more potent contribution to the defeat of isolationism (on the hypothesis that only collisions can produce planetary systems suitable for life) is the relatively new and well-established evidence that the Metagalaxy is expanding. The actual observation is that the galaxies are receding in all directions from each other and that the average density of matter in metagalactic space is steadily decreasing. We need only turn that observation backward and note that yesterday the galaxies were closer to-

gether than today, that a million years ago they were still nearer together, and that a few billion years ago they were all tightly packed together, intermingled, overlapping. They were then far back toward the stage dramatically described as Canon Lemaître's "Primeval Atom." In the early times collisions and disruptive near-approaches must have been millions of times more frequent than would be possible now. In the whole wide world of galaxies there must have been by one method or another innumerable planetary systems established, precariously at first because of the interference of other stars, but ever more safely as the universe expanded.

Billions of Planetary Systems

On the basis of our sampling census of stars in our own galaxy, and our sampling of the galaxy population out to the limit attainable by present telescopes, we can readily compute that there are more than 10^{20} stars in the universe, each one competent of course through radiation to maintain the photochemical reactions that are the basis of plant and animal life. Perhaps only a few percent of these are single stars with planetary potentialities. Perhaps only a few percent of these few. Perhaps only a few percent of these few developed in such a way (nebular contraction) or had such a suitable experience in the past (collisional) that they would now possess persisting planets. Perhaps only a few percent of these that succeed in having stable-orbited persisting planets would have one or more at the right distance from the central star; and of these rightly placed planets but 1 percent have an orbit of suitable circularity to maintain sufficiently equable temperatures. We could go on to a few of the few of the few, because non-poisonous airs and waters are also required, and that particular activity of oxygen, carbon, hydrogen, and nitrogen that we call "living" must get started. We could by such restrictions reduce the number of stars with livable and actually "inhabited" planets to nearly a nothing.

All of these restrictions, however, get us practically nowhere in isolating ourselves as something unique and special, for there are too many stars! Three undeniable factors have entered our consideration — the ordinariness of our sun which has accomplished the creation of life on this planet; the evidence for the universality of the kind of chemistry and physics we know here, and the existence of more than 10^{20} opportunities for life, that is, the existence of more than 100,000 million billion stars.

Let us look once more at large numbers and work this argument over again. Let us suppose that because of doubling, clustering, secondary collisions, and the like, only one star in 1000 has a planetary system. Personally I would think that 1 in 50 would be a better estimate, and many of those who believe in the nebular contraction theory of stellar formation would say that at least 1 out of 10 stars has planets. But to be conservative, we say that only 1 out of 1000 has a planetary system, and then assume that but 1 out of 1000 of those stars with systems of planets has one or more planets at the right distance from the star to provide the water and warmth that protoplasm requires. In our solar system we have two or three planets in such an interval of distance. Further, let us suppose that only 1 out of 1000 of those stars with planets suitably distant has one large enough to hold an atmosphere; in our system we have at least seven planets out of nine with atmospheres. That will reduce our suitable planet to a one in a billion chance.

Let us make one other requirement of our suitable planet: the chemical composition of air and water must be of the sort that would develop the inorganic molecules into the organic. Perhaps that biological evolution occurs but once in a thousand times.

Assembling all four of the one to a thousand chances (all grossly underestimated, I believe, but in the effort to establish our uniqueness in the world, and hence our "importance," we are making it as hard as possible to find other habitable planets), we come to the estimate that only one star out of 10^{12} meets all tests; that is, one star out of a million million. Where does that high improbability of livable planets leave us?

Dividing the million million into the total number of stars, $10^{20} \div 10^{12}$, we get 10^8; that is, 100 million planetary systems suitable for organic life. This number is a minimum; personally I would recommend, for reasons given in Chapter 6, its multiplication by at least 1000, possibly by a million.

To state a conclusion: The scientific researches of recent times have enriched and clarified our concepts of habitable planets. Through discovering the true stellar nature of the spiral "nebulae," and through the deep sounding of star-and-galaxy populated space to such great depths that the number of knowable stars rises to billions of times the number formerly surmised, and also through the discovery of the expansion of the universe with its concomitant deduction that a few billion years ago the stars and planetary materials were much more densely and turbulently crowded together than in the present days of relative calm, we have strengthened our beliefs with respect to the existence of "other worlds." The present concept includes the identifying of our own world as the surface of Planet No. 3, in the family of a run-of-the-mill yellowish star, situated in the outer part of a typical spiral galaxy that contains billions of typical stars — this "home galaxy" being one item in an overall system, the Metagalaxy, that numbers its galaxies in the multibillions.

So much for the peripheral position of our planetary system. So much for the commonness of habitable planets. In the next chapter we turn to the question: "What habitable planets are in fact inhabited?"

CHAPTER SIX

On the Hazards of Primitive Life

It is really of little importance to our main argument whether there are very abundant locations suitable for biology or only 100 planets where sentient organisms live and react to their respective environments. Even this small number establishes the need, in any approach to the interpretation of Nature, of including extraterrestrial life in our cosmic picture. Terrestrialism by itself is limited, useless, and now essentially dead. This viewpoint has come about, and is already gaining wide acceptance, through the impact of three important and relatively recent scientific discoveries. They are the great number of galaxies and stars available for energizing life; the crowded state of the universe a few billion years ago, resulting in the catastrophic birth of numberless planetary systems; and the partial bridging, in the chemical laboratories, of the gap between large and complex but lifeless molecules and the simplest manifestation of continuing life. The discussion of man's Fourth Adjustment in Chapter 8 will describe these three discoveries.

Notwithstanding the little need for further emphasizing the wide spread of protoplasmic operations, it may be well to discuss in more detail the prevalence of life, the hazards it must face, and the possibility of other kinds than ours. The fact that life exists on this undistinguished planet, and arose here naturally, as we shall indicate in Chapter 10, is by itself nearly enough assurance that life is a cosmos-wide phenomenon.

Early Protoplasmic Perils

The argument in preceding chapters maintains that at least one star in a billion will have with it a crusted non-gaseous planet entirely suitable for living organisms. These starlit planets should be as satisfactory for life as is our planet which, with the help of sunlight, has in the course of time developed on its land and in its seas a million kinds of plants and animals. We are

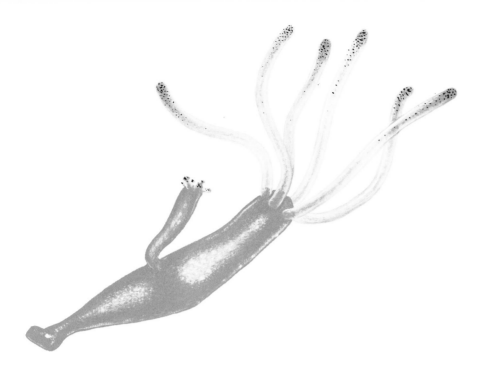

confident from our extensive sampling of the population in distant regions that more than 10^{20} stars exist. Therefore, these suitable one-in-a-billion planets are not at all scarce in the overall stellar universe. There are billions of them.

But it does not follow that just because a planet is suitable for life in having the proper air, warmth, water, and varied chemicals in solution, it will of necessity harbor highly evolved living organisms. It does not follow that all these multimillions of life-bearing planets will have developed highly sentient beings, corresponding to or excelling the best our earth has done. For protoplasm has its perils, especially inexperienced protoplasm.

All living conditions on a planet might appear to be propitious and still nothing happen of high biological significance. That would seem to be extremely unlikely, of course, to one who believes that life is both inevitable and persistent when conditions are right, and the range of rightness is wide. But suppose that in some critical early epoch the air suddenly had so much of the free oxygen that it would burn up the tender molecular combinations striving toward biochemical viability. Or suppose that the cosmic rays from space were too strong, too weak, or too much blocked by atmospheric molecules for them to play a proper part in the initial energizing of the activities required for the combining of the methane, ammonia, water, and hydrogen of the primitive atmosphere into the simplest amino acids. Also conditions might have been adverse to the continuing of life once started. Doubtless on many planets the most elementary organisms for various reasons were stillborn. A report on other atmospheric compositions is given in Chapter 10.

On this planet, life started in the early days of the expanding universe and it has succeeded in holding on and growing. The vegetation early began to take part in changing of the earth's atmosphere, helping to replace the

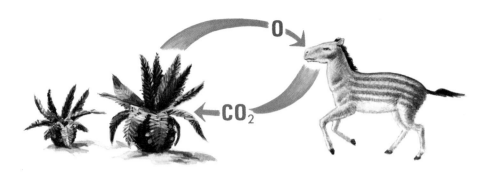

dominant water vapor and hydrogen with the present abundant oxygen. The output of oxygen by plants is now partly balanced by the intake of oxygen by animals; the carbon dioxide exhaled by the animals (assisted in CO_2 production by vegetable decay, fires, and volcanic exhalations) provides the carbon essential for the carbohydrates of the plants.

Probably life got started also on Mars, Planet No. 4. The chemical make-up of the Martian atmosphere and the climatic conditions are considerably different from ours; but there the urge to evolve is as likely, or at least was as likely, as here on No. 3. The oxygen shortage, however, keeps Martian organisms (if any) in low estate. (In Chapter 10 the difficulties of getting born are further examined.)

If among the planets suitable for the higher biological developments there is only one in 1000 that has actually carried its protoplasmic operations to the level we enjoy, that numerical adjustment would still leave us, as shown in the preceding chapter, with at least 10^8 high-life planets — that is, with more than 100 million domiciles of highly developed organisms. We must keep in mind that our sun is average, our stellar associations are not unusual, and our location in space is in no way so special that this particular planet would receive preferred treatment and uncommon opportunities in a biochemical way.

We have cut down from more than 10^{20} to 10^8 the estimated number of stars that feed higher organisms. Many of the other stars may be free of long-continuing biological operations on their planets, or may support only low forms of life. The disqualifications we have suggested on the grounds of star-doubling, poor locations, bad chemicals, and so forth, have been ruthless. We have sought all ways to write off the existence of competition at high levels. The search has been a gesture to those who harbor the wish or thought that Homo may have the distinction that goes with complete uniqueness.

Personally, the writer would multiply the favorable chances for life by a million, accepting the existence of at least 10^{14} high-life planets. There are two principal reasons for this increase by a million times. The first is that we have probably grossly underestimated the number of stars in the universe. The second is that other kinds of life may exist, not only that based on carbon compounds. And such hypothetical life might withstand rough conditions that we could not endure, thus increasing the number of livable planets.

The theoretical considerations by Eddington and later by others suggest that there are not less than 10^{79} fundamental particles (electrons, protons, neutrons) in the universe. The total mass is therefore more than 10^{55} grams,* that is, $10^{79} \div 10^{24}$. Taking as a standard star a mass one-half that of the sun, thus allowing for the vast number of dwarf stars that current researches reveal in the solar neighborhood and which probably exist in comparable abundance elsewhere, we have $10^{55} \div 10^{33} = 10^{22}$ stars. This consideration increases the number of life chances by 100 times over the conservative number, 10^{20}, given above. That this number is much too small can also be inferred from observation. Our sampling of space shows that at least a billion galaxies are within 4 billion light years distance. If they are on the average only one-tenth as rich in stars as our own galaxy, there must be $10^9 \times 10^{10} = 10^{19}$ stars now within our present sampling. A reach to only ten times our present limit would run the number of stars to something like 10^{22}. And that extension of reach is not expecting too much of the future. Between 1915 and 1930 we increased the length of our celestial surveying rod by nearly a million times and therefore increased the explorable volume by the cube of that number.

Other Kinds of Life?

The second argument for a substantial increase in our estimate of the number of planets that are satisfactory for high organic forms is of a different character. It concerns biochemistry rather than statistical astronomy. Omitting details, it can be put as follows:

The life we know and which we have loosely defined on earlier pages is essentially that which, in our mixture of precocious grasp and profound ignorance, we would recognize and designate as life on the surface of any planet we should visit. By surface, we mean to include the land, the atmosphere, the oceans, and other surface waters. Also included are the depths of the oceans and the depths of soils that cover the rocks. In all these

* There are approximately 1.2×10^{24} fundamental particles (protons and electrons) in a gram of matter (counting a neutron as two particles).

The mass of the sun is 2×10^{33} grams. Each "standard" star therefore contains about 10^{57} particles.

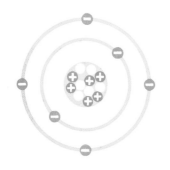

terrestrial locations life is chemically much the same. Carbon compounds prevail; we usually say that our lives are based on carbon, the sixth element in the periodic table.

In its commonest form, a carbon atom is made of six protons with their six positive unit charges, six neutrons that add weight to the nucleus but no additional electric charge, and six nucleus-surrounding electrons with their six negative charges balancing the total positive charge on the nucleus. The six electrons of the carbon atom, according to a standard atomic model, are in two "shells" — the two inner electrons in the so-called K-shell and the other four in the outer L-shell. The electron structure is written 2-4. The next element is nitrogen; it has a 2-5 arrangement, and oxygen 2-6. Because of their electron shell structures, these elements, particularly carbon and oxygen, are easily combined with each other, and with the hydrogen and other elements found in organisms.

In the same vertical group of the periodic table is another very common element; in the earth it is nearly 200 times as common as carbon. It is silicon, which constitutes nearly a quarter of the earth's crust, and in its usual molecular combination with oxygen (sand) makes up about three-fourths of all rock material. Its electron structure is 2-8-4. The outer four electrons, in the M-shell, make of this atom another ready joiner with hydrogen, nitrogen, and oxygen. Like carbon, it can appear in compounds that are gaseous, liquid, or solid. CO_2 is gaseous at room temperatures, but SiO_2 is gaseous only above 2500°C.

These two elements, carbon and silicon, show some other differences, and many similarities in their combinations with other elements. Here we only remark that life based on silicon compounds rather than on carbon compounds would be unlikely, but such is a possibility that we must not overlook. The type of life might be one that we would not readily recognize.

Other elements (like sulphur, electron structure 2-8-6) have been suggested as possible substitutes for oxygen in biochemical evolution. Certainly we must not limit the possibilities of life only to planets with atmospheres, waters, and soils like ours. On the presumption that viable biochemistries other than ours may exist, the number of planets hostile to organic life might thus be considerably reduced.

Adjusting to Unearthly Environments

The gradual adjustment to chemical and climatic conditions that are far different from the kind that terrestrial organisms now experience must be considered as possible. A situation that would today be lethal for us might have become tolerable elsewhere through slow adjustments. Poisons taken in small but increasing dosage sometimes lose their toxicity. If accustomed to ultraviolet radiation over long ages, we could probably stand much more of it than we now endure. Indeed, it is likely that early life on the earth was subjected to very strong ultraviolet radiation, since the present ozone (O_3) barrier some 20 miles above the earth's surface is largely a by-product of the gradual evolution of the planet's atmosphere as vegetation began to release oxygen on a large scale.

Biological adjustment to various physical, chemical, and climatic conditions could widen considerably the life zones around a star. Homo sapiens, for example, is a most adaptable animal and now successfully swarms over the whole earth with the protection of clothing, skin pigments, parasols, and domicile heating. He can go to high altitudes of low pressure with oxygen tanks, and go into the heavy atmospheric pressures in mines and water pressure in ocean depths when outfitted with gadgetry of the proper sorts. Insect life in hot springs, lichens in the polar zones, and marine forms at enormous pressures in the deep seas all testify to the breadth of adjustment and encourage the belief that biological evolution, even if limited to the water-carbon-nitrogen chemistry, can be expected on planets differing considerably from the norm of our present temperate and torrid zones.

Perhaps One Star in Every Million

The foregoing considerations of the climatic extremes that may be tolerated by life and of the possibility of organic origins and evolutions based on other chemical operations have led to the second revision of the numerical probabilities of life throughout the universe, and justify the surmise that an enhancement by a factor of a million is reasonable — that is, we should contemplate the existence of at least 10^{14} planetary situations for life at our level of sentiency. In other words, we surmise that at least one star out of every million supports some kind of high-level protoplasmic operation on

one or more of its planets. Many, but not necessarily all, of these 10^{14} planets may have the plant-animal interdependence in which we ourselves participate.

The carbon and oxygen exchange is in a sense the breath of life — the indispensable inhaling of carbon dioxide by plants and of oxygen by animals, and the exhaling of oxygen by plants and of carbon dioxide by animals. It is a natural cosmic symbiosis.

In the total absence of animals on a planet, vegetation which depends on photosynthesis might soon find the carbon dioxide in short supply; the plants would need to depend for their carbon mostly on erratic volcanos, natural fires, and the products of their own decay.

In the total absence of plants, animals would of course promptly starve; they would in fact never have evolved. As it is, we live together, nutritionally, in happy symbiosis. We animals use the plants for fixing carbon and releasing oxygen — that is, for supplying food and breath; the plants use us as one of the sources of their carbon dioxide, and as fertilizer. It is a natural barter economy.

Life on Planet X

Just where these other life-bearing planets are we cannot now say; perhaps we never can, lost as they are in the glare of their stars, isolated as we are in space, and equipped with sounding apparatus that is still, we hope, primitive. Although not seen or photographed, those other planets are deduced as statistical probabilities. There must be at least 100,000 of them in our galaxy, if we accept the frequency your author prefers.

 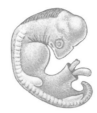 

PARALLELISM

 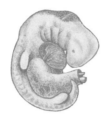 

What kinds of organisms inhabit these other worlds? Are they only plants, animals, and the simpler of non-cellular protista? Or are there other highly developed animate kingdoms? Neither plants nor animals nor in between? If a mature tree should at times pull up its roots and stroll away to a more nutritious or more pleasant locality, or if an animal should give up its motility at times, put down roots and feed itself through the soil and the material provided by photosynthesis, we would indeed be astonished. But equally strange operations are already known to occur in the lower life of the earth's biological display. Chlorophyll, carotin, and xanthophyll may not be the only agents for capturing and using the sun's radiant energy. Our yellowish star radiates the wavelengths that we have grown to need. Redder and bluer suns would cooperate with life forms that prosper in radiation emanating from redder and bluer sections of the spectrum.

Although the life on what we shall call Planet X, an unidentified high-life planet, is a matter for loose conjecture, we should naturally expect it to resemble in many ways some of the myriad life forms on the earth. It is amazing that there are biochemical properties and fundamental growth behaviors that are the same for thousands of kinds of plants and animals that superficially and in bulk differ greatly. Clovers and sequoias have common characteristics in the flow of sap, the structure of their stems, and the functions of their roots and leaves. In mice, whales, and men, the hearts, lungs, and brains are similar in cellular structure and in basic operation. Parallelism, both in evolutionary steps and attained ends, is frequent among the earth's animals, suggesting that such steps are inevitable in biochemical evolution. The inherent properties of atoms and molecules may be such that growing molecular systems and evolving organisms are restrained to develop along specific lines in accord with specific patterns. We might call this an inborn orthogenesis growing out of the properties of organic molecules. We should in that case expect much the same biological operations on Planet X as here, with comparable end results.

The terrestrial social insects, for instance, provide a notable example of parallel development. In many important characteristics the agricultural ants and some species of termites are alike. The two insects are similar in body size, caste system, and the existence among them of sterile workers and egg-laying queens; they are also similar in fungus culture, casting off of the queen's wings, detailed care of the young, and in parasite toleration. Despite these characteristics of astonishing similarity, the termites and ants are not at all closely related. They are phylogenetically as remote from each other as man is from the whale or the bat. But basic chemistries and fundamental physical laws apparently decree that the elaborate organizations of termites, social bees, social wasps, and ants, in their thousands of species, must travel much the same road toward their integrated societies.

A mixing of pure chemical elements will always under the same physical conditions produce the same result, whether it be an odor, an explosion, or a color. Probably we should expect that a mixture of starshine, water, carbon, nitrogen, and other atoms, when physical conditions are fairly similar, will everywhere produce animals that are much alike in structure and operation and plants that have certain standard behaviors, notwithstanding great morphological differences. If we should visit a planet essentially identical with ours in mass, temperature, age, and structure, we would probably not find the biology queer beyond comprehension. We might find it no more peculiar than we would find the biology if we were transported on our own planet into Carboniferous times, or taken back just 150 million years when the great lizards ruled the land and sea, and the birds, mammals, and flowering plants were not yet far developed.

Therefore we surmise that the biology on Planet X and Planets Y, Z, and so forth, might have much in common with the living forms on Planet Earth just because the carbon compounds will have it so, and because the same chemistry and the same natural laws prevail throughout the universe we explore.

CHAPTER SEVEN

Rainbows and Cosmic Chemistry

Notwithstanding many important contributions from biochemistry, including those to which we shall refer in Chapter 10, the mystery of life is not wholly resolved. There are odds and ends to work out, most of them tangled and difficult. But in recent years the progress has been so notable that we might well substitute the word "puzzle" for "mystery," and lay aside the traditional tools of disputation in favor of the keener instruments of biochemistry and microbiology.

Judged by current standards, the early philosophical and theological contemplators of the origin of life were not very successful in convincing themselves or others. A century ago, using biblical argument and metaphysical vocabularies, they fought wordy battles against the biologists, who resorted to verifiable observations — to those lances that so easily penetrate the fondly held theological shields. The biologists, in fact, changed the problem from the misty mystery of the origin of self-conscious man to the clean-cut general question of the origin and nature of all life, of monkeys and mice, of algae and oaks, of everything that crawls, flies, swims, breathes, and metabolizes. As supernaturalism retreated a bit, many scientists overcorrected, unfortunately, and embraced a sterile God-excluding mechanistic philosophy, with the result that the sniping goes on although the major action is concluded and a truce is established.

The astronomer in the past has not been much concerned about the origin-of-life puzzles. He has had his hands full, his eyes and mind full, with inanimate origins. How came the comets? How began the rotation of the galaxy? Why are the planets spaced out as they are? How started the universe? When, where, why? Puzzles aplenty, and except for some rather silly speculations about the Martians, the astronomer has had no concern for the apparently remote problems of biogenesis.

But a change has come about. Many sciences have become involved. The origin and age of the planet, and especially its early history, have become critical factors in the problem of the origin of organisms. The astronomers,

it now appears, have something to contribute. The geologist, by way of paleontology, has always been in congenial touch with those who ask about life and its early career on this planet. The weatherman — especially the paleoclimatologist — has his fingers and imagination in the business. And the physicists, chemists, and mathematicians — they are at the bottom of everything that is material, dynamic, electrical.

The Strange Case of the Self-duplicating Macromolecule requires for a solution, or a substantial approach thereto, the skills of all these specialized detectives, the skills of practically everybody, except perhaps the dogmatic theologian!

But my implication is not quite fair. There are many theologians, still respectful of their doctrines, who profit from the cosmic messages of the sciences. They choose to go along constructively rather than retreat clumsily before the emerging evidence. And the scientists gain from their company, for by them the seeming harshness of cosmic law is softened.

Some theologies are not frozen, not fossilized at a given epoch. Their spokesmen recognize the bearing of the advance of knowledge on the tenability of the ancient doctrines. Some philosophers, not too many, re-examine, re-evaluate, and go forward. By them the cosmologies are re-formed to agree with verifiable discoveries of biology and physics. This evolution of doctrine need not be reluctant, gradual, slow. In situations under human control (like man's own reasoning), beneficent mutations should be welcomed and if possible incited. For change, growth, evolution in this live dynamic universe is inherent and widespread. "If ought were constant in this world/ Thy turn had never come to thee."

Evolution affects not only stars, galaxies, and planetary crusts, animals, plants, and societies, but also touches social policies, touches the ethical systems of man and the religions he fosters. May not science, broadly taken, be the fundamental soil, the cultural soil in which we plant and vitalize our religions? Need so many of them remain dated and non-rational?

On the Evolution of Religious Doctrine

It seems to me appropriate at this point, before we consider extra-terrestrial chemistry in useful detail, to quote a great churchman's views on the verity of mutability and evolution throughout the universe. The following excerpts are from an address given in 1951 by the late Pope Pius XII before the Vatican Academy of Science.

At first sight it is rightly a source of wonderment to recognize how the knowledge of the fact of mutability has gained ever greater ground, both in the macrocosm and in the microcosm, according as science has made new progress, as though confirming with new proofs the theory of Heraclitus: "Everything is in flux": panta rhei. *As is known, our own everyday experience brings to light an immense number of transformations in the world around us, both near and far away, particularly the local movement of bodies. . . . Going still farther, natural science has made known that this chemico-physical mutability is not, as the ancients thought, restricted to terrestrial bodies, but even extends to all the bodies of our solar system and of the great universe, which the telescope, and still more the spectroscope, have demonstrated to be composed of the same kind of atoms. . . .*

Nevertheless, in the face of the undeniable mutability of even inanimate nature, there still rises the enigma of the unexplored microcosm. It seemed, in fact, that, unlike the organic world, inorganic matter was in a certain sense immutable. Its tiniest parts, the chemical atoms, were indeed capable of combining in most diversified manners, but they appeared to be endowed with a privilege of eternal stability and indestructibility, since they emerged unchanged from every chemical synthesis and analysis. A hundred years ago, the elementary particles were still regarded as simple, indivisible, and indestructible. The same idea prevailed regarding the material energy and forces of the cosmos, especially on the basis of the fundamental laws of the conservation of mass and energy. . . . The growing knowledge of the periodic system of chemical elements, the discovery of the corpuscular radiations of radioactive elements, along with many other similar facts, have demonstrated that the microcosm of the chemical atom, with dimensions as small as a ten millionth of a millimeter, is a theater of continuous mutations. . . .

The very first modest attempt to break down the nucleus (of nitrogen) goes back to hardly more than three decades ago, and it is only in recent years that it has been possible, by bringing into play tremendous forces, to produce very numerous processes involving the formation and the breaking down of nuclei. Although this result — which, insofar as it contributes to the cause of peace, is certainly to be inscribed among the glories of the century — represents in a field of practical nuclear physics no more than a preliminary step, nevertheless it provides for our considerations an important conclusion, namely, that atomic nuclei are indeed, by many orders of magnitude, more firm and stable than ordinary chemical compositions, but notwithstanding this they are also, in principle, subject to similar laws of transformation, and hence are mutable.

At the same time it was possible to establish that such processes have the greatest importance in the economy of energy of the fixed stars. In the center of our sun, for example, according to Bethe, and in the midst of a temperature which goes as high as some twenty million degrees, there takes place a chain-reaction, returning upon itself, in which four hydrogen nuclei combine into one nucleus of helium. The energy thus liberated comes to compensate the loss involved in the radiation of the sun itself. . . .

If the scientist turns his attention from the present state of the universe to the future, even the very remote future, he finds himself constrained to recognize, both in the macrocosm and in the microcosm, that the world is growing old. In the course of billions of years, even the apparently inexhaustible quantities of atomic nuclei lose utilizable energy and, so to speak, matter becomes like an extinct and scoriform volcano. And the thought comes spontaneously that if this present cosmos, today so pulsating with rhythm and life, is, as we have seen, insufficient to explain itself, with still less reason, will any such explanation be forthcoming from the cosmos over which, in its own way, the shadow of death will have passed. . . .

If we look back into the past at the time required for this process of the "Expanding Universe", it follows that, from one to ten thousand million years ago, the matter of the spiral nebulae [galaxies] was compressed into a relatively restricted space at the time the cosmic processes had their beginning.

To calculate the age [of the solid crust of the earth from the age] of original radioactive substances, very approximate data are taken from the transformation of the isotope of uranium 238 into an isotope of lead (RaG), or of an isotope of uranium 235 into actinium D (AcD), and of the isotope of thorium 232 into thorium D (ThD). The mass of helium thereby formed can serve as a means of control. This leads to the conclusion that the average age of the oldest minerals is at the most five thousand million years. . . .

The pertinent facts of the natural sciences, to which We have referred, are awaiting still further research and confirmation, and the theories founded on them are in need of further development and proof before they can provide a sure foundation of arguments which, of themselves, are outside the proper sphere of the natural sciences. This notwithstanding, it is worthy of note that modern scholars in these fields regard the idea of the creation of the universe as entirely compatible with their scientific conceptions and that they are even led spontaneously to this conclusion by their scientific research. Just a few decades ago, any such "hypothesis" was rejected as entirely irreconcilable with the present state of science.

Cosmo-chemistry and the Astronomer as Detective

We return from these remarks on nuclear physics, the age of the earth, and related subjects to our observation that many scientific disciplines are involved in the technical work on the so-called mystery of life. The astronomer enters the operation in two ways. First, he can contribute information and rational speculation on the age of the fossil-bearing rocks and the probable temperature conditions on the earth's surface in earlier millennia. His second contribution develops from the attempt to look beyond this planet's organisms, and inquire about the spread of biochemical evolution elsewhere. We have already argued the case for the existence of myriads of suitable planets throughout metagalactic space. The question now is: What is the likelihood that habitable planets are in fact biologically occupied? We are not specifying what the nature of the life may be, whether closely resembling some terrestrial forms, or basically different. The difference might arise from oxygen scarcity, hydrogen over-richness, atmospheric density too high or too low, or from other conditions that would guide biochemical evolution in ways other than those terrestrial.

It is amazing what grand thoughts and great speculations we can logically develop on this planet — thoughts about the chemistry of the *whole* extraterrestrial universe — when we have such a tiny sample here at hand. We can analyze chemically only the meteoric samples that we pick up. The earth is composed of 6000 quintillion tons of air, water, and rock (chiefly rock). This quantity, however, is trifling compared with the contents of the sun, which has 330,000 times as much matter: and the sun is but one of 100 quintillion stars. In fact, we can actually examine chemically only a small fraction of the earth's crust. It may be many years before we have bored a hole into the interior. We know the oceans pretty well and the lower atmosphere, but what a minute sample that is on which to base the grand extrapolations.

The infalling meteorites add little now to the mass of the earth; and they tell us little that we do not already know. Through chemical analyses they do show that there is probably nothing new under the sun, or near it, no chemical elements in meteorites that we do not find in the solar atmosphere or in the earth's crust. Some of the minerals in meteorites are in combinations different from those we find on earth, but we have not been deep into the earth where pressures are high and where the relative proportions of elements differ from those near the surface. The large meteorites are fragments that may have come from the interior of a planet long ago fractured. But they contain no kinds of atoms that are unknown to us on this planet.

Nucleons from outer space, chiefly protons, continuously bombard our upper atmosphere and some in the guise of cosmic rays get through to the surface; and of course mass-carrying starlight and some radio waves reach the earth's surface from outer space. But only the meteorites bring outside information of a sort suitable for chemical analysis. No samples from Mars or Jupiter are at hand, and as yet no rock or dust from the nearby moon. As matters stand, it looks as if we experience a severe and nearly complete

isolation from the rest of the universe about which we are so curious. Certainly the isolation is complete for the moon-seeking moth and for the sun-fed plants, and for the animals that we like to call *lower* than man — lower in intellect if not in curiosity. They are earth-bound.

Our rather hopeless separation from the stars and indeed from neighboring planets prevailed until about a century ago when chemistry went to the heavens by way of the spectroscope and man was suddenly in material contact with the sun, stars, and glowing nebulosities. No longer need he fret about his isolation. Interstellar distances were no longer a deterrent to knowledge of the chemistries of the widespread cosmos.

This is how the wonder came about; and we start to sketch the story with some ancient human history and proceed through rather technical concepts that can scarcely be avoided if we are to grasp very important conclusions about the nature of the universe and man.

Rainbows and Stellar Spectra

The rainbow with its spread of colors and its association with storm clouds and the mists of waterfalls and fountains has been throughout the ages a mystifying spectacle. The primitives of Nias, for example, "tremble at the sight of a rainbow, because they think it is a net spread by a powerful spirit to catch their shadows."* To the ancient Hebrews it stood as a pledge against the recurrence of catastrophic world-wide floods.† But it has a deeper meaning, a more certain significance to Cosmography; it is a clue to the composite nature of light — a clue that was not followed up until recent centuries.

The refraction of light by water drops, where the amount of the deviation depends upon the wave length of the light, was recognized as the source of the rainbow's colors long before the astronomers made use of this

* Sir James George Frazer, *Taboo and the Perils of the Soul* (London, 1936), p. 79.
† *Genesis* 9: 13.

principle in the analysis of starlight. But the complete and correct theory, which explains that the solar spectrum is shown in the rainbow, was not easily or rapidly attained. Aristotle and Seneca missed; Grosseteste of Oxford and Witelo the Silesian, in the thirteenth century, A.D., hit the right theme — raindrop refraction. Later came Theodoric of Freiburg with the interpretation of different combinations of refraction and reflection for the primary and secondary rainbows. He was followed by many who improved the theory, including big-name scientists like Descartes, Edmund Halley, Newton, Thomas Young, and Astronomer Royal George B. Airy, who in 1838 left little unexplained. The rainbow, however, although incited by the sun, is an earth-bound meteorological phenomenon, and our current interest is in starlight as a guide to cosmic chemistry.

In 1666 Sir Isaac Newton's experiments with prisms of glass and with sunlight that had passed through a narrow slit into a dark compartment demonstrated that light is composed of all colors, each color having its own refrangibility (bending). The sun's spectrum was not recognized in all its power, however, until Wallaston of London and the German scientists Fraunhofer and Kirchhoff detected and interpreted the interruptions in the continuous spectrum — the "breaks between the colors." The breaks were first recognized as dark lines with no explanation, then correctly as absorption lines, and then as clues to the kinds of chemical atoms in the sun's atmosphere. By these scientists and their followers the fertile new Age of Spectroscopy was opened a century ago. Laboratory analysis of light showed that each substance, such as sodium, sulphur, calcium, and iron, when properly heated and excited, had a different pattern of bright radiations of specific wave lengths, a pattern of specific positions along the spectrum.

In the solar spectrum these patterned radiations become dark absorption lines. That is, the various kinds of atoms in the sun's atmosphere block (absorb) specific wave lengths of the sun's whole-spectrum radiation. Atoms of an element radiate and absorb in the same wave lengths; the continuous background radiation they absorb is produced by the hot body of the sun.

Nothwithstanding the growing evidence yielded by the early spectroscopes that the lines in the solar spectrum were indicators of the chemical composition of the sun's atmosphere, a famous European scholar, Auguste Comte, declared a century and a quarter ago that we should *never* be able to know the chemistry of the stars. Only a few decades later Sir William Huggins in England, Father Secchi in Rome, and others were reporting on the chemical composition of the brighter stars. With the arrival, in the astronomer's kit of technical tools, of the photographic plate as an accurate recorder of starlight, the classification of stars, bright and faint, on the basis of their chemistry became big business. At the beginning of this century the work largely centered at the Harvard Observatory in the hands of Antonia Maury and Annie J. Cannon, with special contributions coming from the Lick Observatory in California, from Potsdam in Germany, from Poulkova in Russia, and the Vatican Observatory. Philosopher Comte's dictum notwithstanding, extraterrestrial chemistry emerged and soon dominated the science. This remarkable outcome well illustrates the adage that it is not good for the reputation of one's judgment and imagination to say and believe that anything cannot *ever* be done.

Everywhere: the Same Chemistry, the Same Physics

A few further statements on the chemistry of stars, as shown by spectrum analysis, will assist in our orientation among the atoms. To those who find the language rather technical, I suggest that this section be skipped. The last sentence of the chapter states the major conclusion.

1. Only the surface of a star, of course, can be directly studied through the analysis of light, but astrophysical theory and mathematical "boring tools" boldly plunge beneath the surface and lead us to report confidently on the chemical composition that must exist far down to account, first, for the kind of spectrum we find at the surface and, second, for the total brightness of the star.

2. Miss Cannon's classification puts the stars into 60 different classes and subclasses, arranged in order of surface temperature. The temperature prescribes the presence or absence of the various spectral lines, and also determines the color. Red Betelgeuse, a cool giant star, has a spectrum rich

in absorption lines; yellowish Polaris has many fewer, and bluish Rigel is so hot at the surface that only the lines of hydrogen and helium are prominent. More recent work in America and Sweden has increased the number of classes by adding to Miss Cannon's temperature-based classification a sub-classification that depends on the intrinsic luminosity (candle power) of a star, thus providing in the description of stellar spectra a sort of second dimension. This subclassification is very useful in estimating the absolute luminosities and subsequently the distances of many types of stars.

3. About 20 percent of the stars, according to the large sampling provided by Miss Cannon's catalogue, are similar to our sun in spectrum; therefore more than 40,000 neighboring stars are sun-like in color and sur-face chemistry. This proportion probably holds on the average throughout our galaxy and others, but with a higher proportion of solar stars in the nuclei of galaxies than in their spiral arms.

4. The integrated spectra of whole galaxies are naturally difficult to photograph clearly. So far as we have studied them, however, they are what we would expect — a composite of all spectral classes. They are, in fact, much like the sun's spectrum, Class G0, which is in the middle of the spectral series that runs from hottest Class B to coolest Class M.

5. Some of the spectra of individual stars in remote galaxies are now known; they are in all details like those of stars in our galaxy — an observa-tion that again emphasizes that a common chemistry prevails throughout the universe we explore. In the nearest of the external galaxies, the Star Clouds of Magellan, the spectra of hundreds of stars have been photographed. All are of familiar types. All the many classes of stars and nebulosities found in the Magellanic Clouds have their counterparts with us.

6. In these two nearest of galaxies, which are irregular in form, being neither symmetrically spiral nor smoothly spheroidal, are found nearly all the familiar kinds of stars that are variable in light emission. Their spectral classes range from reddish M and N (long-period variables), through yellow-ish K, G, and F (classical cepheids), to A and B at the hot end of the spectrum.

7. Among the variables are eclipsing binaries, mostly of spectral classes A and B. Such doubles can be analyzed through studies of their light variations. Their masses, relative motions, temperatures, densities, and sizes can be calculated from the characteristics of their light curves. We find that

the same celestial mechanics, the same gravitational and radiational laws, in brief, the same physics, prevails in these other galaxies as here at home. We are led to the important generalization that we have a common physics as well as a common chemistry throughout the whole of the explorable universe.

8. Finally, in these comments on the knowledge that the multi-colored rainbow has led us to, attention is called to another ancient observation, which now baffles us much less than it baffled our remote ancestors. This newer clarity has also come through spectrum analysis. I refer to the Sword of Orion, and its hazy central star. The spectroscope has been able to "loose the bands of Orion" by showing what Job could not know, namely, that the Orion Nebula is a mass of oxygen, hydrogen, carbon, and nitrogen gas, which is excited into radiation by the super-hot stars of its vicinity.

The spectroscope has, in fact, revealed the wide distribution in interstellar space of the gaseous stuff that stars are made of; and, of higher significance at this point in our exposition, it shows that such shining nebulous material exists also in the Megellanic Clouds and the Andromeda Galaxy, and indeed throughout the Metagalaxy. This is an important revelation in that it indicates that the universe is not yet completed, and may never be. It suggests that probably galaxies as well as stars and planets are being formed currently in response to the natural laws of gases, celestial motions, and light propagation — laws that we already understand pretty well.

Radio Signals from Outer Space

As a postscript to this chapter on orientation by way of the spectrum, it is appropriate to mention that the recently developed radio telescopes, working in wave lengths from a centimeter to 30 meters and longer, have entered the field miraculously. (I use that word loosely, since miracles connote the supernatural which is here hardly an acceptable concept.) For example, the large radio-wave receivers find in all parts of the Metagalaxy, from the nearby spiral arms of our own system out to clusters of galaxies a hundred million light years distant, the weak radiation from cold interstellar and intergalactic hydrogen atoms. The existence of these radiation waves, 8 inches from crest to crest, was first predicted from atomic theory, then they were detected in our Milky Way. In a rush they were exploited by

radio astronomers and electronic engineers in Australia, Holland, and America. Here is a listing of some of the recent discoveries of radio astronomy, all of which have cosmographic relevance:

1. The Magellanic Clouds are found to be embedded in a low-density medium of neutral hydrogen, that is, neutral in electric charge, in contrast to ionized hydrogen such as that which helps illumine the Orion Nebula.

2. The spiral arms of our own galaxy have been traced by discovering the excess of neutral hydrogen within them in contrast to that in the areas between the arms.

3. The expansion of the universe is confirmed through finding a consistent red shift in radio waves that are half a million times longer than the visual light waves where first the red shifts were discovered and measured.

4. The existence in interstellar space of drifting dust, which is one component in the composition of evolving stars, is confirmed through the radar detection of innumerable meteors in the earth's atmosphere.

5. Natural radio "signals" are now received from some of the planets, notably from Jupiter's cloudy surface. Powerful electric storms in and around Jupiter's so-called red spot are a suspected source of the signals. Do we have here the thunderbolts of Jove?

6. The sun, the Milky Way, the wrecks of supernovae, and hundreds of unidentified "radio stars" in remote space all contribute signals in the measurable radio frequencies, making this new phase of astronomical science sensational, if not miraculous.

It is advisable to add that the use of the word "signal" does not imply a belief that any of these impulses originate with a living being. Radio signals need not always require biological agents. Lightning provides a signal, as do whirling sunspots, and they both have natural physical causes.

To summarize the last two sections in a single sentence: Spectroscopes, radio telescopes, scientific methodology, and the mathematics of the physical scientist have joined in revealing a uniformity of structure, of composition, and behavior throughout the cosmos. They guarantee to the searcher on Planet No. 3 that he can reasonably assume that what holds here holds widely.

CHAPTER EIGHT

The Fourth Adjustment*

In the past history of the evolving human mind, with its increasing knowledge of the surrounding world, there must have been a time when the philosophers of the early tribes began to realize that the world is not simply anthropocentric, centered on man himself. As society developed, the village attained central significance — a natural view supported first by the evidence of a circular horizon and second by the increasing vagueness of the world as one increases the distance from home. But the higher civilizations of the Near and Middle East (and perhaps elsewhere) became increasingly conscious, a few thousand years ago, of the daily revolving sun, stars, and wandering planets. The navigators detected evidence of the curvature of the surface of the oceans and of the earth. The sphericity indicated thereby led to the belief that the center of the earth rather than a locality on the surface was the center of the visible universe. This view was thought to be consistent with the apparent motions of the moon, planets, sun, and stars. The *geocentric* concept thus became the common doctrine in many of the most civilized nations. It is often labeled the Ptolemaic theory.

This first adjustment of man to the material universe was only mildly disturbing to his self-conscious ego, for man appeared, on pretty good evidence, to surpass all other living forms. He saw little reason, therefore, to be openly humble. He personally was not central in the universe, but his earth seemed to have that distinction.

* This chapter is adapted from an article that appeared in *The American Scholar*, Autumn, 1956. In several places it paraphrases the discussion in other chapters of the present volume.

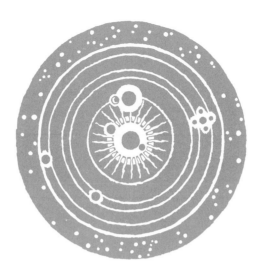

From Geocentric to Heliocentric

The second adjustment was the abandonment of this earth-center theory. The new hypothesis was not generally acceptable in the Western world until the Copernican Revolution of the sixteenth century soundly established the heliocentric concept. The liberal philosophers and eventually the church fathers yielded to the scientists' theory of a universe centered on our sun. It was a slow shift, for man is a stubborn adherent to official dogma. In time, however, he accepted the sun as the center not only of the local family of planets but also of the total sidereal assemblage; and he long held that view. But it, too, was a fallacy. Another shift was in the making as soon as the sun was recognized as an ordinary star; but not until modern telescopes reported on globular star clusters, galaxies, and cepheid variables did this further adjustment become imperative.

The earth-centered cosmology had been given up, in favor of the sun-centered theory, very reluctantly. And likewise, later, in spite of increasing evidence requiring a further change, the scientists, philosophers, and laymen held doggedly to the heliocentric view. Was this because of vanity — because of the feeling, cultivated by the unscientific dogmatists, that man is of paramount significance in the world of stars and space-time?

From Heliocentric to Sagittarius and Beyond

There are several better reasons for this erroneous concept — for this heliocentric theory; they are quasi-scientific explanations of what can be observed. For example, the Milky Way lies along a great circle: it is a band of star-composed light that divides the sky into two practically equal parts. Also, it is of about the same brightness in all parts. By implication, therefore, the sun and earth are centrally located. A second evidence is that the numbers of stars seemed to the early census-takers to fall off with distance from the sun in

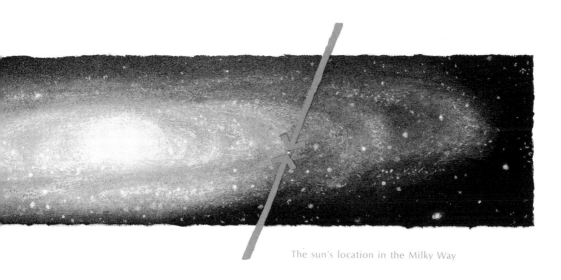

The sun's location in the Milky Way

all directions as though it were central; and such a position for his star among the stellar millions brought to man a dignity of location that was not at all disagreeable. But again it was an illusion.

As late as 1917 the leaders in astronomical interpretation held that the sun was central, or at least very near the center of the sidereal universe. (The galaxies were then not recognized officially as other great stellar systems.) The introduction of the period-luminosity relation for cepheid variable stars as a sounding tool, and the determination of the distances and distribution in space of the globular star clusters, first indicated the eccentric position of the earth, sun, and surrounding stars in the flattened stellar system — in the stellar discoid made manifest by the star-crowded Milky Way.

Gradually came other probing evidences that the billion-starred nucleus of our spiral galaxy is remotely distant through the southern constellations of Sagittarius, Ophiuchus, and Scorpio. Suffering from these new thrusts into the stellar depths, the heliocentric theory of the stellar universe struggled briefly, weakened and died.

The center of the galaxy is not near at hand among the bright stars that define those southern constellations for they are but a few hundred light years away. The center of our galaxy, we have found, is more than twenty-five thousand light years distant. The billions of stars in that nucleus together make the extended white glow in the southern Milky Way which we call the great Sagittarius star cloud.

The shift from the geocentric to the heliocentric concept doubtless had some philosophical impact in the sixteenth century, but not a great deal. The hot, turbulent, gaseous sun would be no place for the delicate array of biological forms in which man finds himself at or near the top. Earth-center or sun-center seemed to make little difference to cosmic thinking. From the death bed of Copernicus to the birth of this century and later the prevailing

EGOCENTRISM

heliocentric concept of the stellar universe incited little if any philosophical uneasiness.

But then, with the rapidly increasing accumulation of astronomical information, came the inescapable need for this third adjustment — one that should have deeply affected and to some extent has disturbed man's concern about his place, his career, and his destiny.

The shift of the sun and earth to the edge of our galaxy has considerably eroded human pride and self-assurance; it has carried with it the revelation of the appalling number of comparable galaxies. We could accept rather cheerfully the Darwinian evidence and argument for our animal origin (even though the theologians of a century ago found it strong medicine), for that evidence still left us, we believed, at the summit of all terrestrial organisms. But the abandonment of the heliocentric universe, on the basis of dependable astronomical evidence, was certainly deflationary from the standpoint of man's position in the material world, however flattering such advances of human knowledge were to the human mind.

The "galactocentric" hypothesis puts the earth and its life on the outer fringe of one galaxy in a universe of millions of galaxies. Man becomes peripheral among the billions of stars of his own Milky Way; and according to the revelations of paleontology and geochemistry, he is also exposed as a recent and probably ephemeral manifestation in the unrolling of cosmic time.

At this point we pause for a sombre or happy thought, one that is sombre or happy depending on one's mood. With the advance of science, and with the retreat of superstition and belief in the supernatural, we have in recent centuries gone so far and so firmly in our orientation of man in the universe that there is now no successful retreat! The inquiring human mind has passed the point of no return. We cannot restore geocentrism or even heliocentrism.

The apes, eagles, and honey bees, with their specialized skills and wisdoms, may be wholly content to be only peripheral ephemerals, and thus miss the great visions that open before us. For them egocentrism and lococentrism may suffice; for us, no! And since we cannot (and would not) go

LOCOCENTRISM

back to the cramped but comfortable past without sacrificing completely our cultures and civilizations, we go forward; and then we find that there is another chapter to the story of orientation. Geocentrism was not sufficient; nor is heliocentrism.

Another shift must be made, for we are concerned in this discussion not only with the location of our earth in the time and space of the physical world, but with our location in the world of biological phenomena.

The downgrading of the earth and sun and the elevation of the galaxies is not the end of our progress as scientific pilgrims, plodding through philosophical fields. As intimated on previous pages, the need for a further jolting adjustment now arises above the mental horizon. It is neither wholly unexpected by workers in scientific fields, or wholly the result of one or two scientific discoveries. It is a product of the age. We turn from astronomy to the overlap of a dozen other sciences and ask about the spread of life throughout the universe. As unsolicited spokesman for all earthly organisms of land, sea, and air I ask the piquant question: "In this universe of stars, space, and time, *are we alone?*"

Biological Orientation

From among the many thoughts and measures that promote this Fourth Adjustment of Homo sapiens in the galaxy of galaxies, three phenomena stand out as most meriting our further consideration. The first refers to the number of stars, the second to catastrophes of ancient days, and the third to the origin of self-replicating molecules. They are worth brief summarizing at this point although the first two have been to some extent presented in earlier chapters, and the third will be the main theme of Chapter 10.

To the ancients only a few thousand stars were known; to the early telescopes, however, a million; and that astounding number has increased spectacularly with every telescopic advance. Finally, with the discovery that the so-called extra-galactic nebulae are in fact galaxies, each with its hundreds or even thousands of millions of stars, and with the inability to touch "meta-

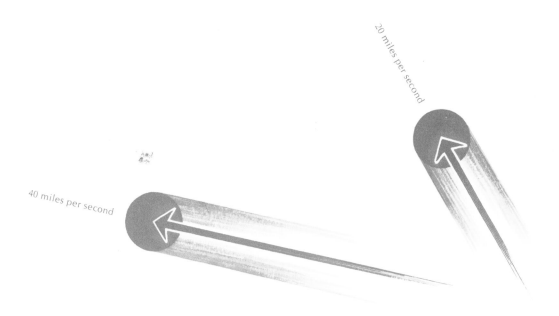

galactic bottom'' with the greatest telescopes, we are led (as shown in Chapter 6) to accept the existence of more than 10^{20} stars in our explorable universe, perhaps many more.

(The numbers of stars and their ages are of course not humanly comprehensible in the usual number terms — too many stars, too much space, too many years for our minds, which are accustomed to operate in serially countable numbers. The Macrocosmos transcends our counting. And comprehension is not simplified when we turn to the atomic Micro-cosmos and point out that in our next breath we shall each inhale more than 1000 million million million atoms [10^{21}], of oxygen, nitrogen, and argon.)

The second phenomenon, the expanding Metagalaxy, bears on the question: Do planets accompany at least some of the stars that radiate energy suitable for the complex biological activity that we call life? — a question that was asked and tentatively answered in Chapter 5.

We now accept the strong observational evidence of a universal redward shift in the light received from distant external galaxies, and accept also the interpretation of that red-shift as a result of the scattering and diffu-sion of galaxies and the expansion of the universe. The speed of the mutual recessions is about 20 miles a second for galaxies separated by a million light years; twice as fast for galaxies at twice the distance apart; three times at thrice the distance, and so on. The exact numerical values are still under investigation and revision, as is the possible failure to maintain at a very great separation this increase of scattering speed with distance.

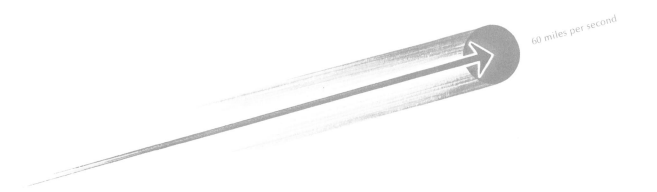

60 miles per second

The Turbulence of Long Ago

The present rapid dissipation of the Metagalaxy in all directions naturally turns thought to the situation of a year ago when the galaxies were closer together, and to a century, a millennium, a billion years ago. There was, of course, as we go back in time, an increasingly greater concentration of the now spreading cosmic units (galaxies). The average density of matter in space at present is very low — something like 10^{-30} grams per cubic centimeter, which by terrestrial standards is a veritable super-super-vacuum. A few thousand million years ago, however, the average density in the unexpanded universe must have been so great that collisions of stars and gravitational disruptions of planets, stars, and nebulae were inevitably frequent.

At that time countless millions of other planetary systems must have developed, for our sun is of a very common stellar type. Stars of non-solar types must have also participated in the cosmic turmoil.

Now here is an important coincidence. The crust of the earth, radioactively measured, is also a few thousand years old. Therefore the earth and the other planets of this planetary system were born in those crowded days of turbulence and disastrous encounters.

(Our sun, an ancient compared with many blue and red giants, is so ordinary that in Miss Cannon's famous spectrum catalogue we find some 40,000 sun-like stars, all in our immediate neighborhood.)

Other ways in which planets may be formed, other than by this slam-bang process of the earliest and most crowded times, have been proposed by astronomers and other scientists (Chapter 5). For example, the gravitational contraction of proto-stars out of the hypothetical primeval gas and dust, giving birth to the proto-planets on the way, is an evolutionary process now widely favored. It would imply the existence of countless planets.

The head-on collision theory of planetary origin has been favorably considered in various versions. But the stars are now so widely dispersed that collisions must be exceedingly rare — so very unlikely, in fact, that we might claim uniqueness throughout all creation for ourselves if planet birth depended only upon collisional procedure, such as could now occur. But that vanity of uniqueness cannot be easily maintained, since the expanding universe discovery has shown the crowded conditions when our earth emerged out of chaos.

Passing over details, we again state the relevant conclusion: *Millions of planetary systems must exist,* and *billions* is the better word. Whatever the methods of origin, and doubtless more than one type of genesis has operated, planets may be the common heritage of all stars except those so situated that planetary materials would be swallowed up by greater masses or cast off through gravitational action.

In passing, we recall that astrophysics has shown that our kind of chemistry and physics prevails throughout the explorable universe (Chapter 7). There is nothing uncommon and special here or now.

Remembering our 10^{20} stars and the high probability of millions of planets with suitable chemistry, dimensions, and distance from their nutrient stars, we are ready for the question: On some of these planets is there actually life? Or is that biochemical operation strangely limited to our planet — limited, that is, to No. 3 in the family of the sun, which is an average star located in the outer part of a galaxy that contains 100,000 million other stars — and this local galaxy but one of millions of galaxies already on the records?

Is life thus restricted? Of course not. We are not alone. And we can accept life's wide dispersion more confidently when our third observation is indicated.

To summarize in four sentences what we shall spell out in some detail in Chapter 10: Biochemistry and microbiology, with the assistance of geo-

A: physics, astronomy, and other sciences, have gone so far in bridging the gap between the inanimate and the living that we can no longer doubt that whenever the physics, chemistry, and climatology are right on a planet's surface, life will emerge, persist, and evolve. The mystery of life is vanishing. Objective science is replacing the subjective miraculous. The many researches in the past few years in the field of macromolecules and microorganisms have now made it quite unnecessary to postulate miracles and the supernatural for the origin of life. We must adjust our world view to the wide spread of life.

The step in human orientation that I call the Fourth Adjustment is ready for the taking, if we care to explore that opportunity. The scattering of galaxies, the abundance of stars, and the structure and habits of macromolecules on warm, moist, starlit planetary surfaces have prompted this further and most important adjustment in the understanding of the place and functioning of life in the universe. The acceptance of the evidence and argument that the biological development on this planet is not unique and that varied and highly elaborated sentient life is abundant and widely distributed has led to this most important step of all in the orientation of Homo in the material world.

Have we come now to the end of the journey, or are there other steps ahead? In view of the rapid growth of scientific techniques and the continual exercise of the human imagination, it would not be wise to suggest that we shall *never never* find need for a further adjustment in our knowledge of man's place in the universe — that we shall never discover a reason for an orienting adjustment that transcends both the physical and biological orientations which are now represented, respectively, by the third and fourth adjustments.

A fifth adjustment might be in the psychological realm, or in the "negative matter" world, or in one of those fanciful existences where our Metagalaxy is only an atom in some superuniverse, or in the equally droll (and equally possible) existence where our electrons are the galaxies in some microcosmic universe that is below our measures and our knowing.

CHAPTER NINE

A Digression on Great Moments

Cosmic energy, in the form of sunshine and the earth's leaking body heat, and in cooperation with the materials of the "primeval soup" in the earth's primitive shallow seas, provided long ago for the origin and evolution of green leaves and green stems, and for the eventual development of the higher plants and animals. In this cooperation the early and continuing biochemical reaction called photosynthesis was dominant. Here we point to the beginning of the collaboration of radiant energy and organic molecules as a decisive step in the life episode on the terrestrial surface. It was the start of Operation Chlorophyll, without which we would not be. So far as life is concerned, it was indeed one of the Great Moments of the universe; if it could happen on this planet, it could happen elsewhere, with perhaps equally momentous consequences.

The idea of a particular Great Moment, a critical turning point in the manifold evolution of the material universe, is an intriguing thought. We have college courses on Great Ideas, reading lists of Great Books, and books on Great Men. There are Great Expectations, Highlights of the Year, and so on. Why not look for the Great Epochs in Cosmography?

Before the primitive plants got established, the earth's rocky crust was essentially barren biologically, as the moon's crust is now; and then photosynthesis began to function, an operation for which we shall always be grateful. What are other equally revolutionary episodes? They may be for the most part too hidden for us to detect, for we are considerably impotent and ignorant in the face of Nature's complexities. But some of the Great Moments are clearly discernible.

Different choosers of epochal events would probably make different choices. I suggest the following:

1. The explosion of the all-including Primeval Atom (if there was one) — a violence that according to current hypotheses has resulted successively in the expanding universe, the birth of the heavy chemical atoms, and the formation of galaxies and stars; and resulted also in the origin of planets, some of which, with moist and rocky surfaces, were suited for the emergence of varied organisms, among which are those that speculate on Great Moments.

2. The fortunate "cooperation of charm and countercharm" (as an ancient Chinese saying puts it) that permitted natural laws to provide for the existence of the cohesive atomic nucleus. That concept is a rather hard one — it takes a bit of grasping. I am reminded that a famous modern physicist who explores the nature of atomic nuclei once confided that it is only by a narrow squeak that matter exists at all.

But perhaps this ubiquitous nuclear coherence is not a Moment; it does not involve the one-directional passage of time; it should be listed with Momentous Facts rather than with factual moments.

3. The lightning strokes, or other natural energy manifestations, that helped to synthesize the amino acids out of the pre-primeval atmosphere of the earth, where methane and ammonia, water vapor and hydrogen gas prevailed. The amino acids underlie the proteins, which underlie organisms. This means, in short, Nature's synthesis of the first continuing life — or at least the vital first step toward the origin, on the earth or elsewhere, of "material organizations perpetuating their organization."

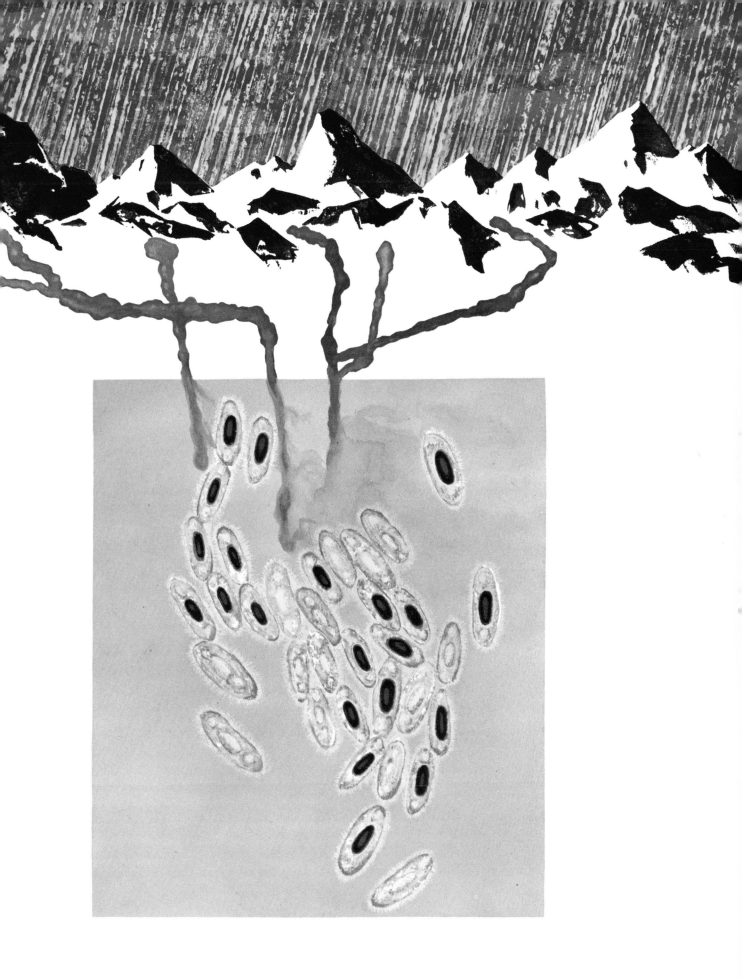

4. The aforementioned invention or "accident" of photosynthesis, including its becoming a biological habit. This complicated biochemical device brought life's energy down from the sun.

5. The issuance from the shallow waters of seashore, lake, and river of primitive animals that were learning to take their oxygen raw — an occurrence of some 400 million years ago for this planet, perhaps much later or earlier for many others. Some of these primitives that crawled or flopped ashore were the forerunners of insects; some were the ancestral frogs and other early amphibia. Below the surface of the water the primeval plants and animals got their necessary oxygen, which burns and builds, in diluted dosage. They found it captured by waves and ripples from the overlying air. On land this inhaling of concentrated oxygen was an early accomplishment of major moment.

The specialized breathing apparatus developed variously. For instance, we higher mammals long ago abandoned our ancestral gills and developed in their stead a bellows arrangement (lungs) equipped with strings (vocal cords) which permits talk and song in addition to the natural traffic in oxygen and carbon dioxide. In other words, a happy by-product of the development of an efficient apparatus for inhaling needed oxygen and exhaling undesired carbon dioxide was the production of an ingenious vocal means of communication. For the transfer of information to one another it made us not chiefly dependent, as are the ants, on the twiddling of antennae, or dependent, as are the bees, on the waggling of our abdomens.

6. The "invention," that is, the rapid mutational development, of insect wings. These appendages, which have made the mighty class of Insecta so dominant (a million kinds, a trillion individuals), and in many ways so important in the life of the planet, did not arise through the slow

adaptation of existing appendages to a new use. The wings of flying mammals (bats) and of flying neo-reptiles (birds) have arisen through the adaptation and evolution of the forelegs. The insect wings were acquired without the sacrifice of standard appendages. They are something entirely new and extra, and serve in part as an escape mechanism. The survival since the Paleozoic Era of many orders of insects was doubtless dependent on their overcoming some of the precariousness of life on the ground where they could not easily escape their devourers by running, jumping, crawling, or hiding. Those primitive insects that could take to the air on occasion, long before there were birds to exploit the art of traveling in a gaseous medium — those early winged insects passed one important test for the survival of the species; they got away! Their escape mechanism was indeed novel and well designed.

We could list additional items, such as the descent of our ancestral Hominidae from the trees, the discovery of the uses of fire, the announcement of the laws of motion and of gravitation. But some of them, like insect wings, may be too local to be considered as Great Moments for the total universe. Most of those numbered above obviously involve gradual changes, not sudden unique inventions. In fact, it might be better to use the word "epoch" or "era" rather than "moment."

Incidentally, if partial comprehension and description of the cosmos is in itself a part of Cosmography, and if such comprehension is an important item in the whole cosmic scheme, then the big mutations in the primate's forebrain are master moments, and so was the discovery of the axis of the wheel, and of the calculus, and the subconscious. But let's skip this anthropocentricity and get back to the stars and the emergence of organisms.

CHAPTER TEN

Toward the Emergence of Organisms

It is not enough simply to assert the apparent inevitability of the emergence of life on a planet's surface when conditions are right — when the chemicals proper for protoplasm are available; the mass, temperature, and motions of the planet are suitable; and the weather is good. That is not enough. To say that biochemical evolution is natural and insistent is not the whole story. We must report further on how Nature builds up self-replicating molecular aggregates and detail some of the steps in this process.

The subject of life's origination has a sultry history. Incompetent observations, and a willingness to make silly deductions, kept alive for centuries the thesis that low forms of life could spontaneously arise from filth. Pasteur helped kill that heresy. He and his fellow scientists for a time were opposed by a few scientific critics. But the worst bombardment of the scientific advance against mystery in the origin of life came from the religious fortifications, which were stubbornly defended by cloth and laity. It was stoutly held that although man could make alloys in his laboratories that Nature had not made, and could develop new hybrids of plants and animals, and create societies, he was, is, and always will be impotent in the production of the biologically alive. He could destroy life, visible and invisible, but the original creation of life was held to be exclusively in the inscrutable hands of the Almighty. To seek the origin of life was to peer into forbidden places; it approached the blasphemous.

Thus cramped by dogma, science had to enter into research on human origins indirectly, by way of studies of the simplest organisms and the nature of life at its threshold. The dogmatic ceased to prevail rather long ago. In the past century our knowledge of the universe has expanded so profusely in its many phases and dimensions that ancient prophecies can no longer even with "interpretation," encompass it all. The biochemists and the microbiologists of the twentieth century now effectively observe, experiment, and speculate on the beginnings of the primitive life which the sedimentary rocks report was already here a billion years ago.

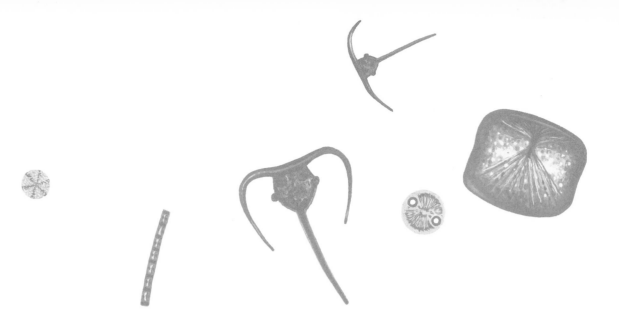

Pioneering by Oparin and Haldane

Ignoring magic and foreswearing superstition, J. B. S. Haldane ventured in 1928 an essay in which he called attention to the probable early conditions, physical and chemical, on the surface of the earth, and their suitability for the natural synthesis of the animate out of the inanimate. The primitive atmosphere of the earth, it is now widely (but not universally) believed, was free or almost free of oxygen in an uncombined gaseous state. Oxygen is a hungry element and takes every opportunity to combine with receptive atoms. In the form of H_2O (water) and SiO_2 (silica) there was always much terrestrial oxygen — in fact, oxygen is one-half the crust of the earth; nine-tenths of the oceans, lakes, and rivers; and nearly a quarter of the present atmosphere. But in early times the air had little free oxygen. The thousand trillion tons now in the earth's atmosphere have come in considerable part during the past billion years from the "breathing" of vegetation. Free oxygen is a by-product of photosynthesis, supplemented somewhat by the breaking up of water vapor molecules by short-wave solar radiation in the upper atmosphere.

Water vapor and hydrogen gas were dominant in the earth's primitive atmosphere, along with carbon dioxide (CO_2), methane (CH_4), and nitrogen in the form of ammonia gas (NH_3). Methane and ammonia still appear in the atmosphere of the cold planet Jupiter; they are practically gone from the earth's air. Free oxygen and free nitrogen now constitute about 99 percent of the earth's atmosphere. The original prevailing water vapor condensed, as the planet cooled, into lakes, oceans, and wet soils.

The absence from the earth's primitive atmosphere of atomic and molecular oxygen would indicate of course that ozone, the triple form of oxygen, was then also absent. Such absence must have been of considerable biogenetic significance, for the *ozone barrier* in our atmosphere, some 20

The primitive, minute diatoms and
dinoflagellates have silica-rich outer shells.

miles above us, now benevolently protects us tender growths from lethal
ultraviolet radiation; it was probably not appreciably present in the early
times, 2 to 4 billion years ago. Throughout long eons it may have still been
thin and penetrable, and became really effective only when photosynthetic
vegetation had released oxygen in large amounts from water vapor and
carbon dioxide.

The chief importance of the early lack of ozone was that the short-
wave ultraviolet radiation from the sun could then bring energy of special
potency into the shallow waters (whenever water vapor clouds did not
obstruct). The penetrating ultraviolet radiation was no doubt one of three
or four sources of energy that could participate in the generation of primitive
life. The others are atmospheric electrical discharges (lightning), gamma
radiation from decaying radioactive elements, and possibly the issuing body
heat of the earth, such as the heat from geysers and volcanoes.

Short-wave radiation, as H. J. Muller and others have shown, expedites
biological mutations. In pre-ozone days the ultraviolet radiation may have
greatly speeded and diversified organic evolution. Now such accelerated
evolution is blocked by the ozone barrier.

Haldane's pioneer speculation on early conditions suitable for the
emergence of terrestrial life refers to the energy in short-wave radiation:

*Now, when ultraviolet light acts on a mixture of water, carbon dioxide,
and ammonia, a vast variety of organic substances are made, including sugars,
and apparently some of the materials from which proteins are built up. This
fact has been demonstrated in the laboratory by Baly of Liverpool and his
colleagues. In this present world such substances, if left alone, decay — that
is to say, they are destroyed by microorganisms. But before the origin of life
they must have accumulated till the primitive oceans reached the consistency*

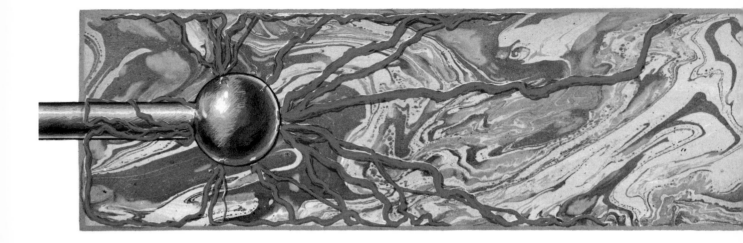

of hot dilute soup. Today an organism must trust to luck, skill, or strength to obtain its food. The first precursors of life found food available in considerable quantities, and had no competitors in the struggle for existence. As the primitive atmosphere had little or no oxygen, they must have obtained the energy they needed for growth by some process other than oxidation — in fact, by fermentation. For, as Pasteur put it, fermentation is life without oxygen.*

Independently of Haldane, the Russian scientist A. I. Oparin was meditating some 40 years ago on the origin of life. He was unhampered by religious preconceptions. Already in 1923 a preliminary booklet was published by him in Russian: 13 years later his volume *On the Origin of Life* appeared. The book has become a classic. The 18-page introduction by S. Morgulis to the second edition of the English translation is in itself an important contribution to the subject. Since 1950, as Oparin's analysis has become more widely known, several important researches related to biogenesis have been carried out. Studies in photosynthesis, and biochemical work on amino acids, nucleic acids, and viruses entered the field. Powerful electron microscopes analyze the macromolecules. In particular, the experimental work of Stanley Miller, in Dr. Harold Urey's laboratory at the University of Chicago, is noteworthy. He assembled a sample of the assumed primeval terrestrial atmosphere, composed of the gases methane, ammonia, water vapor, and hydrogen, bombarded it with an electrical discharge (simulating

* *Science and Life* (London, 1928).

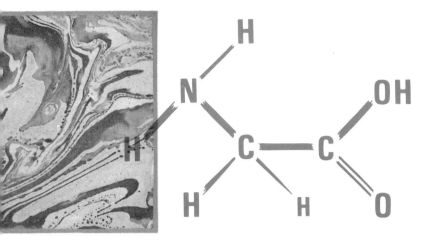

the primeval lightnings), and produced amino acids and other organic compounds. These amino acids, as mentioned previously, are the all-important constituents of organisms.

The experiment has been repeated and extended in laboratories at Yale University, the Carnegie Institution of Washington, Oak Ridge laboratories, and elsewhere. It will be much extended, for through this simple experiment we have made a long step across the ground that separates the unquestionably inanimate from the unquestionably alive. Miller's report on his pioneer synthesis of the molecular bases of life appears on page 000.

The thoughts of Oparin and his translator on the subject of the emergence of life can best be presented in a few trenchant quotations — all of them rich in meaning to anyone who would grope in the dim past for answers to basic questions of cosmogony. Necessarily, technical terms must be used, and the general reader may therefore prefer to skip some of the following quotations.

To begin with, biochemist Oparin emphasizes the fact that the long-enduring assumption that well-organized life first came through supernatural creation is irrevocably dead. Also the thesis that life was coeval with matter cannot be maintained — and the evolution of inanimate molecular matter cannot be denied. The astrophysicist would add that atoms, as well as molecules, have also evolved in the past, and indeed are even now evolving in hot stars and novae.

The remainder of this chapter is given over to quotations from Oparin, Morgulis, and Miller.

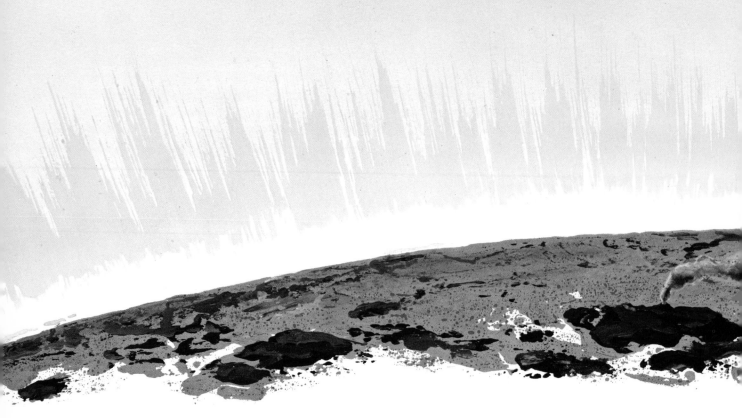

One must first of all categorically reject every attempt to renew the old arguments in favor of a sudden and spontaneous generation of life. It must be understood that no matter how minute an organism may be or how elementary it may appear at first glance it is nevertheless infinitely more complex than any simple solution of organic substances. It possesses a definite dynamically stable structural organization which is founded upon a harmonious combination of strictly coordinated chemical reactions. It would be senseless to expect that such an organization could originate accidentally in a more or less brief span of time from simple solutions or infusions.

However, this need not lead us to the conclusion that there is an absolute and fundamental difference between a living organism and lifeless matter. Everyday experience enables one to differentiate living things from their non-living environment. But the numerous attempts to discover some specific "vital energies" resident only in organisms invariably ended in total failure, as the history of biology in the nineteenth and twentieth centuries teaches us.

*That being the case, life could not have existed always. The complex combination of manifestations and properties so characteristic of life must have arisen in the process of evolution of matter. A weak attempt has been made . . . to draw a picture of this evolution without losing contact with the ground of scientifically established facts.**

* A. I. Oparin, *The Origin of Life*, translation and introduction by S. Morgulis (2nd ed.; New York: Dover Publications, 1953), pp. 246, 247.

As the Earth Cooled Off

Whatever natural method of planetary origin actually prevailed for our own system, there can be little doubt but that the earth's crust passed through a stage of molten or at least hot rocks, and certainly a stage of hot atmosphere. As a consequence, there was for a time more hydrogen, helium, and other gases of light atomic weight escaping into space than at present; but otherwise the earth's chemical composition involved the same kinds of atoms as now. The molecular compounds, however, were evolving as the rocks, oceans, and air were giving up their heat to the cold of interstellar space.

It is beyond doubt that during the [earliest history of the earth] (especially during the early period of the existence of hydrocarbons) the physical conditions on the earth's surface were diffrent than now: the temperature was much higher, the atmosphere had a different composition, light conditions were different, etc., but in this there is nothing unusual or mysterious. Quite the contrary, these conditions are more or less well known to us and we can not only easily picture them to ourselves but we can even reproduce them, to a large extent, in our own laboratories. Nevertheless, they do not furnish an explanation of how life had arisen on our Earth. And it is not difficult to understand this because knowledge of the external physical conditions is not sufficient for the solution of the problem of the origin of life.

It is also necessary to take into consideration the inherent chemical properties of the substances from which, in the last analysis, living creatures

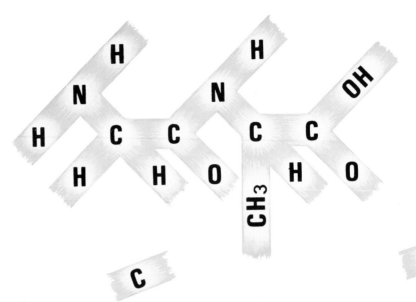

were formed. The study of the behavior of those substances under given external influences will indicate the path which the evolution of organic substance has followed. This approach to the problem is justified especially by the fact that only at the beginning of this evolutionary process were the environmental conditions of existence different from those of our own natural environment. From the time when the primary ocean came into being, the environment in which organic substances existed resembled our own so closely that we may safely draw conclusions about the progress of chemical transformations on the basis of our knowledge of what is happening today. [Oparin, pp. 105-106.]

Thus it came about, when our planet had cooled off sufficiently to allow the condensation of aqueous vapor and the formation of the first envelope of hot water around the Earth, that this water already contained in solution organic substances, the molecules of which were made up of carbon, hydrogen, oxygen and nitrogen. These organic substances are endowed with tremendous chemical potentialities, and they entered a variety of chemical reactions not only with each other but also with the elements of the water itself. As a consequence of these reactions complex, high-molecular organic compounds were produced similar to those which at the present time compose the organism of animals and plants. By this process also the biologically most important compounds, the proteins, must have originated. [Oparin, p. 248.]

Adventures in the Hot Thin Soup

As noted on earlier pages, an all-satisfying definition of life is not easily attained. "Molecular organizations perpetuating their organizations"

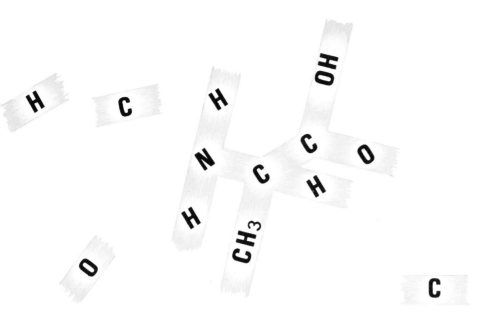

is a rather lifeless attempt, even if we underscore perpetuating. Morgulis objects to the phrase "Origin of Life" for it suggests a single or sudden event — a leap from the inanimate to throbbing life — which most certainly is not correct; a better phrase, he suggests, for the title of Oparin's book would be "Life's Coming into Being." But this writer would boggle at that word "being."

To most people Life connotes something that crawls, creeps or at least wiggles if not by means of well-articulated appendages at any rate by temporary protoplasmic protrusions, or cilia, or delicate flagella. Life need not perhaps be visualized in the form of a stalking elephant but to the layman it may seem inconceivable except as some unicellular organism of microscopic dimensions. But even the most primitive unicellular organism has a complexity of structure and function that staggers the mind and is removed from the beginnings of life by a genealogy extending for millions upon millions of years. Possibly, as Oparin so convincingly tells us, it all began some 2 billion years ago as a venture in colloidal systems of microscopic size separating from the "hot thin soup," to use Haldane's happy description of the primordial ocean.

The biologist, unlike the layman, knows no lines of demarcation separating plant life from animal life, nor for that matter living from non-living material, because such differentiations are purely conceptual and do not correspond to reality. [Morgulis, pp. vii-viii of the translator's introduction to Oparin's book.]

The origin of life was not an occurrence ascribable to some definite place and time; it was a gradual process operating upon the Earth over an

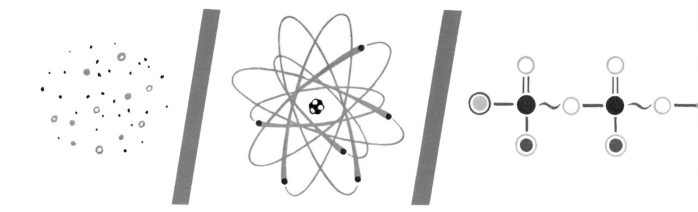

inconceivably long span of time, a process of unfolding which consumed perhaps more millions of years than was required for the evolution of all the species of living things. It is one of Oparin's great contributions to the theory of the origin of life that he postulated a long chemical evolution as a necessary preamble to the emergence of life. One might think of the evolutionary process passing through three distinct chemical phases, from inorganic chemistry to organic chemistry, and from organic chemistry to biological chemistry. [Morgulis, pp. vi-vii.]

As long as the cell is considered as the unit of life, the origin of life must remain a paradox. But like the erstwhile atom in chemistry, the cell has lost its prestige as the ultimate unit in biology. Both the atomic and the cellular theories have become obsolete. The cell, like the "indivisible" atom, is now recognized as a highly organized and integrated system built up from extremely small and distinct particles. Whether the ultimate particles of life have been found and identified is very doubtful, some of the units themselves being highly organized entities, but the concept of a cell as a unit of life has been thrown out of the window together with the atom. [Morgulis, p. xvi.]

Thermodynamically directed chemical evolution could conceivably proceed indefinitely without changing from a non-living to a living state. Only when organic matter had achieved a high degree of organization, and had acquired diverse propensities through the concatenation of such substances (with chance as the only arbiter) did primordial life emerge as a new dimension in nature: matter perpetuating its own organization. Natural selection, operating upon chance variations, set the evolutionary direction along numerous pathways which living things have followed irresistibly. [Morgulis, p. xxii.]

From Lifeless to the Living

If we ignore the rigorous standards of physics for the moment, we can argue that this universe is multi-dimensional — not simply a space-time scheme. A possible dimension that might require additional natural laws is

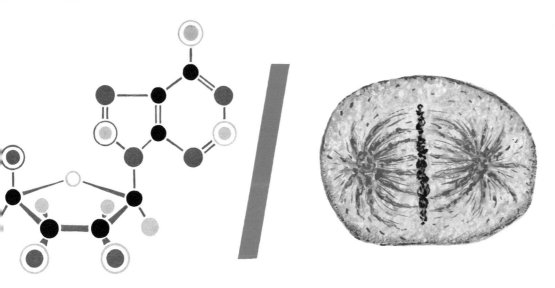

Consciousness; another is Life. The latter certainly involves biochemical regulations more complex than are obvious in the laws of the standard space-time world. Oparin points to the new properties that have been uncovered in biochemical evolution, the new colloidal-chemical order that has been imposed on the more simple organic chemical relations. These new properties are a cue, a clue, and a challenge. They may lead to a description and definition of life that satisfies chemist, biologist, and perhaps even the philosopher.

This brief survey purports to show the gradual evolution of organic substances and the manner by which ever newer properties, subject to laws of a higher order, were superimposed step by step upon the erstwhile simple and elementary properties of matter. At first there were simple solutions of organic substances, whose behavior was governed by the properties of their component atoms and the arrangement of those atoms in the molecular structure. But gradually, as a result of growth and increased complexity of the molecules, new properties have come into being and a new colloidal-chemical order was imposed upon the more simple organic chemical relations. These newer properties were determined by the spatial arrangement and mutual relationship of the molecules. Even this configuration of organic matter was still insufficient to give rise to primary living things. For this, the colloidal systems in the process of their evolution had to acquire properties of a still higher order, which would permit the attainment of the next and more advanced phase in the organization of matter. In this process biological orderliness already comes into prominence. Competitive speed of growth, struggle for existence and, finally, natural selection determined such a form of material organization which is characteristic of living things of the present time. [Oparin, pp. 250-251.]

The origination of life was a transition from organic to biological chemistry, from lifeless to living matter, from the inanimate to the animate realm of Nature. But what is Life? Is it some new property of organic matter *acquired in the course of evolution or is it something which resulted from the organization of organic matter? Irritability, motility, growth, reproduction may be good aids to differentiate a live from a dead organism but it is questionable whether these represent the fundamental properties of primordial life. There is good reason to think that a certain period of the Earth's history must have been marked by complete sterility, i.e., absence of organisms; therefore, the fundamental property or properties of living systems must have appeared in highly complex protein macromolecules antedating the appearance of cellular organisms.*

Proteins containing nucleic acid are the only constituents of organisms which are known to possess the capacity to grow and to reproduce directly by self-duplication or by replication. But as organic compounds they can neither grow nor reproduce. Neither viruses nor genes, both of which represent nucleo-protein systems, can duplicate or replicate themselves unless they are incorporated within a suitable cell or nucleus. Considered simply from the point of view of capacity to reproduce, are these nucleoproteins living or non-living systems? [Morgulis, p. xi.]

A touch of Darwinian evolutionary principle has entered the primitive pre-cellular phase of life. The survival of the best-adapted prevails not only with plant, man, and beast, but also in the microcosmos.

Natural selection has long ago destroyed and completely wiped off the face of the Earth all the intermediate forms of organization of primary collodial systems and of the simplest living things and, wherever the external conditions are favorable to the evolution of life, we find countless numbers of fully developed highly organized living things. If organic matter would appear at the present time it could not evolve for very long because it would be quickly consumed and destroyed by the innumerable microorganisms inhabiting the earth, water and air. For this reason, the process of evolution of organic substance, the process of formation of life sketched in the preceding pages, cannot be observed directly now. The tremendously long intervals of

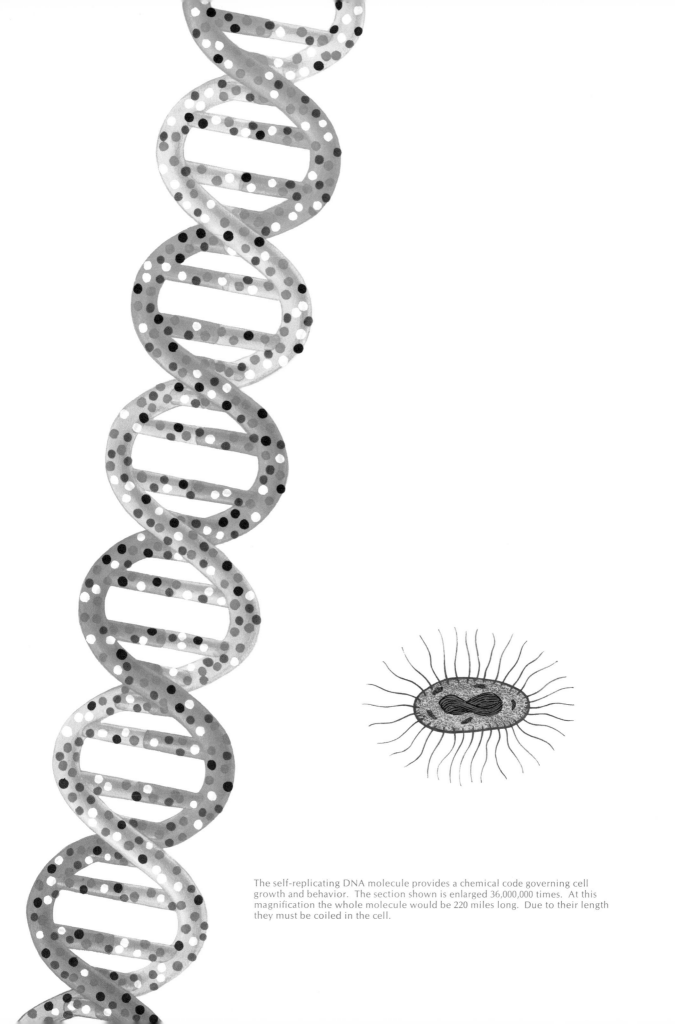

The self-replicating DNA molecule provides a chemical code governing cell growth and behavior. The section shown is enlarged 36,000,000 times. At this magnification the whole molecule would be 220 miles long. Due to their length they must be coiled in the cell.

*time separating the single steps in this process make it impossible to repro-
duce under available laboratory conditions the process as it occurred in
nature. [Oparin, p. 251.]*

*The conditions of the Earth during the past couple of billion years
have undergone such radical alterations that biogenesis may no longer be
possible. However, as Oparin points out, even if biogenesis were operating
at the present time, the innumerable predatory organisms which populate
the Earth would quickly destroy the products of biogenesis. [Morgulis, p. x.]*

The concluding paragraph of Oparin's volume carries a note of cau-
tion about celebrating too soon, and a note of conviction that the goal is
attainable.

*We are faced with a colossal problem of investigating each separate
stage of the evolutionary process as it was sketched here. We must delve into
the properties of proteins, we must learn the structure of colloidal organic systems, of enzymes, of protoplasmic organization, etc. The road ahead is hard
and long but without doubt it leads to the ultimate knowledge of the nature
of life. The artificial building or synthesis of living things is very remote, but
not an unattainable goal along this road. [Oparin, p. 252.]*

Theory Put to the Test of Experiment
Because of the historical importance of Stanley Miller's work, mentioned above, I give in full the abstract of his report.* The highly technical

*J. Am. Chem. Soc. 77, 2351 (1955).

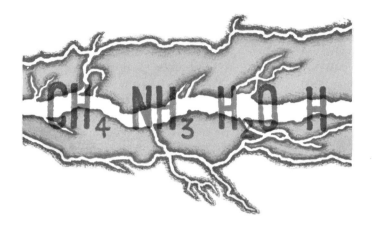

details and specialized language will indicate to the reader the sophistication and difficulty of biochemical research on problems dealing with the emergence of living organisms.

A mixture of gases, CH_4, NH_3, H_2O and H_2, which possibly made up the atmosphere of the Earth in its early stages, has been subjected to spark and silent discharges for times of the order of a week to determine which organic compounds would be synthesized. Several designs of apparatus and reasons for their construction are described. Analyses of the remaining gases were made and CO, CO_2, N_2 and the initial gases were found. A red compound that seems to be associated with the trace metals is formed, as well as yellow compounds, probably polymers, which have acidic, basic and ampholytic properties. The mixture of compounds is separated into acidic, basic and ampholytic fractions with ion exchange resins. The amino acids are chromatographed on Dowex-50 and the acids on silica. Glycine, d, l-alanine, β-alanine, sacosine, d, l-α-amino-n-butyric acid and α-amino-isobutyric acid have been identified by paper chromatography and by melting points of derivatives. Substantial quantities of several unidentified amino acids and small amounts of about 25 amino acids are produced, while glycolic, d, l-lactic, formic, acetic and propionic acids make up most of the acid fraction. Quantitative estimates of these compounds are given. Evidence is presented that polyhydroxy compounds of unknown composition are present. HCN and aldehydes are direct products of the discharge. Although there is insufficient evidence, the synthesis of the hydroxy and amino acids may be through the hydroxy and amino nitriles in the solution. The relation of these experiments to the formation of the Earth and the origin of life is briefly discussed.

From his cautious discussion of the results of the experiments, which indicate what might have happened a few thousand million years ago, I excerpt a few sentences.

If these experiments are to any degree a representation of the reducing atmosphere of the Earth, then we see that not only would the formation of organic compounds be easy, but that most of the carbon on the surface of the Earth would have been in the form of organic compounds dissolved in the oceans. . . .

These ideas are of course speculation, for we do not know that the Earth had a reducing atmosphere when it was formed. Most of the geological record has been altered in the four to five billion years since then, so that no direct evidence has yet been found. However, the experimental results reported here lend support to the argument that the Earth had a reducing atmosphere; for if it can be shown that the organic compounds that make up living systems cannot be synthesized in an oxidizing atmosphere, and if it can be shown that these organic compounds can be synthesized in a reducing atmosphere, then one conclusion is that the Earth had a reducing atmosphere in its early stages, and that life arose from the sea of organic compounds formed while the Earth had this atmosphere. This argument makes the assumption that for life to arise, there must be present first a large number of organic compounds similar to those that would make up the first organism. . . .

This reasoning, coupled with the independent argument that hydrogen is so abundant in the universe, places the assumption of a reducing atmosphere on sufficiently firm basis that it should be taken into account in future discussions of both the formation of the Earth and the origin of life.

A highly important extension of Miller's work on the synthesis of the organic compounds that must have been the forerunners of living organisms is reported from the Geophysical Laboratory of the Carnegie Institution of Washington by Philip H. Abelson. In setting up hypothetical "primitive atmospheres," he tried out mixtures other than the methane, ammonia, water vapor, and hydrogen used by Miller, with the result that always amino acids were synthesized. For example, he successfully replaced ammonia with nitrogen, and methane with carbon monoxide and carbon dioxide, gases that the early volcanoes must have supplied in abundance. Here is the compact abstract of his report (*Science,* Nov. 9, 1956):

> *Simulating atmospheric conditions that might have been present early in the history of the earth, amino acids such as alanine, β-alanine, glycine, and sarcocine have been synthesized employing a variety of compositions. Combinations of gases, including $CO_2 — N_2 — H_2 — H_2O$, $CO — N_2 — H_2 — H_2O$, $CO_2 — NH_3 — H_2 — H_2O$, were subjected to electric discharges, and in each case amino acids were formed. The earlier work of S. Miller employing $CH_4 — NH_3 — H_2O$ has been confirmed.*

Several other recent contributions from the physiological, chemical, and virological laboratories could be cited, as well as earlier shrewd speculations on the origin of life, but the foregoing quotations and arguments should suffice to show that biogenesis is no longer a hazy field of investigation. The evolution of macromolecules is natural, and apparently eager! As Dr. George Wald has remarked, just give the right molecules a chance in a suitable environment; we do not have to do everything for them; they do a great deal for themseles.

CHAPTER ELEVEN

The Human Response
to an Expanding Universe

In the middle third of this century we have attained to such a huge body of knowledge about the universe that basic alterations in our frontage on the future appear necessary and in fact inevitable. The sciences are responsible, along with the philosophies that are aware of the meaningful contributions from science.

In the Microcosmos the physicist now dismembers the atom and measures the quantum, and the biologist unravels the mysteries of the gene. In the Macrocosmos the astronomer records an expanding universe of billions of galaxies, each with its billions of stars, and the mathematician has regularized beautiful concepts concerning the interiors of stars and the history of space-time.

The recession of the galaxies, which leads to the expanding universe deduction, the colossal number of stars ($> 10^{20}$) which are potential suppliers of energy for generating and maintaining planetary life, and the new biochemical revelations about the natural emergence of the living from the inanimate — these three discoveries establish firmly our belief in the cosmos-wide occurrence of life. When we add the discovery that the sun, planets, and naked-eye stars are indifferently located at the edge of one ordinary galaxy, we establish man's place in the universe as less extraordinary than his vanity pictured it a brief century ago.

Before we venture some remarks on what might be the human response to an expanding world of galaxies, and to an explosively expanding knowledge of atoms, genes, stars, and natural laws, a foundation can be laid: first, by examining the possibility of man's long survival on the earth; and, second, by surveying the intellectual equipment that might be capable of understanding cosmic behavior, and constructively responding thereto.

THE
HUMAN
RESPONSE
TO
AN
EXPANDING
UNIVERSE

117

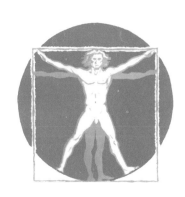

Fish or Homo — That Is the Question

The protoplasmic experiment, as we may designate life, is an effective demonstration of Nature's intricacies. We are probably much more complex in body and mind, much more wonderfully made than we know. The human imagination, versatile as it is, would be hard put to dream up such complexities and coordinations as those we now discover inside the living cell, and it would also be far surpassed by full knowledge of the true mechanism at the center of a single molecule. Fiction lags behind the facts. The yet undiscoverable, the still unknown but not unknowable, so far transcends the what we know that a very rich and happy future of inquiry and discovery lies ahead.

To me it is a sign that we are sincere subscribers to the "growth" motif that threads and spreads through the universe, to the growth certainly of mind if not of body, to the evolution of races if not of individuals, when we inquire what lies ahead for mankind; what lies far, far ahead in the times when the galaxies will have scattered widely, the moon receded to its coming faintness, and the massive mountains of the earth have been worn away by the persistently weathering winds and rains. What then of the sun and the earth? What of terrestrial biology? What then have *we* grown into?

Since men in the future must continue to rely for survival on their natural wits and acquired wisdom, and since they are embattled in a continued contest with a Nature that includes their dangerous selves, we are led to worry and wonder whether proud man or the meek will eventually inherit the earth. As an example of the meek I might choose the fish. They chiefly employ instincts and not heavy forebrains.

Fish or Homo — that is the question. Which animal type will be here 10,000 years from now? Which will more likely fall victim of fate and folly? The answer of course is too obvious. The fish have been here several hundred million years; man but a few hundred thousand. The oceans are stable enough in their salinity, temperatures, and food supplies to suit indefinitely a thousand species of fish. It is difficult to imagine a way of curtailing the life of that class of animals without the complete disruption of the planet, or the poisoning of the plankton food on all the seven seas. But 10,000 years is a *pretty* long time for Homo. His structure and social manners do not make him a good insurance risk. How will he eventually be dispossessed? That is the immediate topic of our conjectures.

What Opposes Man's Survival?

About three-fourths of the earth's crust is under the oceans; the remainder protrudes above the water level to various heights. There is a measurable advance and recession of the shore lines. Some of the mountains rise a little through the continuous wrinkling of the earth's crust, and they are worn down by the winds and rains. In general, however, the continents seem to be fairly stable over the geological areas. Extrapolating into the future, we should say that it is extremely unlikely that man will be drowned out of existence by the rising sea or desiccated by the lack of water. A man-eliminating deluge is not in the cards, nor is a totally lethal drought.

Let us take a wide view and consider sketchily the project of a complete extermination of the human race. In what manner might we, as the versatile agents of Nature (or the devil!), proceed to the elimination of Homo sapiens?

First we set a time limit — not too short, not too long. Let us examine the probability of men still being on the earth's surface 10,000 years from now.

THE
HUMAN
RESPONSE
TO
AN
EXPANDING
UNIVERSE

119

We begin with the macrocosmic instruments of eradication. What is the possibility of the collision of the earth with ordinary stars? If the earth, or even the sun, were struck by one of those stellar bodies our assignment would be completed; terrestrial biology would be erased. But the stars are so widely separated that collisions are out of the question in our chosen relatively short time interval of 10,000 years. The probabilities are overwhelming against our having trouble with stars.

We appreciate that easy escape and ask about the sun cooling down enough to freeze us out, or blowing up into a nova and incinerating the planets. No likelihood at all, or at least very highly improbable, for the sun appears to be of the relatively quiet type of star, and its radiation has been steady for many hundreds of millions of years. Its life depends on its hydrogen fuel, and the hydrogen content is ample to supply radiant energy, produced by atomic fusion, for a million times the duration we have chosen for this survival problem.

Safe from annihilation by stars and sun, should we fear the earth's misbehavior, such as its abandoning orbital regularity, getting too near the sun or too far away? The answer is "No." Our mathematical analyses show that the planetary orbits are completely stable over time intervals such as those we are here considering. The earth moves in what is practically a vacuum in a nearly circular path around the sun, and neither will its daily rotation nor its yearly revolution change perceptibly in the span of 100 centuries. (We can, of course, adapt ourselves to the coming and going of the ice sheets, such as those that occurred in the northern hemisphere during the past 100,000 years.)

Already we have mentioned the relative constancy in the heights of continents and depths of oceans. Terrestrial life has readily adjusted itself

to the ups and downs of land and sea in the past million years, and in our prescribed 10,000 years the slowly moving mountains and shore lines will present little danger to Homo.

The poisoning of the earth's atmosphere with an overabundance of volcanic gases, making it unbreathable by land animals, including man — well, such has not happened in the past 500 million years and it is certainly unlikely in the next 10,000; the earth is gradually getting over its eruptive birth-pangs.

Outer space has some dangers — gases, meteors, and cosmic rays. But the spoiling of our atmosphere through conflict and pollution with interstellar gas and dust is a very long chance. The gas is mostly non-poisonous hydrogen and helium, and its abundance is so little that our nitrogen-oxygen atmosphere shields us completely. It protects us also from the tiny high-speed interplanetary meteors, and from lethal radiations.

To summarize the progress so far in this project of eliminating man (and other animals) from the earth's surface, we get no likely help from the stars, from interstellar dust, from the sun's radiation or its lack, from the deviation of the earth from its present orbit, from deadly climates, or from the chemistry of the earth's air, land, and water.

We go to the biological sciences. The large beasts are no longer a threat, nor, in fact, any of the plant and animal forms. We are now competent also to cope with bacteria, viruses, and the like — at least sufficiently well to keep our species going.

Of course catastrophe, fatal and world-wide, *could* happen, the disaster coming anywhere from star crash to infective protein; but the chances are heavily against it — less than one chance in a million, I would surmise for trouble with astronomical bodies; less than one in a thousand

THE
HUMAN
RESPONSE
TO
AN
EXPANDING
UNIVERSE

121

for serious difficulties with climates, volcanoes, world-wide floods or desiccations; and perhaps less than one chance in a hundred for planet-wide incurable disease.

Even if 99 percent of the world's population of Homo sapiens should fall foul of sudden disaster, there would yet be left more than 25 million humans rapidly reseeding the earth. The total elimination effort would have been fruitless. Spoiling a culture or a civilization is one thing, and perhaps not too arduous; complete eradication of a widespread species is quite another, and vastly more difficult.

To restate his position, I would say that man seems to have a healthy prospect, a long security from stars, climate, and terminating germs. But wait! I have not named the real danger, and it is bleakly ominous, as every one in these days recognizes. The danger is man himself! He is his own worst enemy. He is acquiring tools and studying techniques that might soon solve the problem we set — the complete elimination of Homo from the planet earth.

Much could be written on various methods of man's elimination of himself. Something could be ventured on the defenses against such a grim danger, but that is not a responsibility of this particular essay. Rather, it is the responsibility of everyone who desires to justify, for our species of Homo, the name *sapiens*.

The Generic Mind

We who read, write, and contemplate have minds that have been laboriously taught. The instruction has been done by books and teachers, and by our own efforts. Through such instruction we have attained a considerable degree of competence and self-assurance. We can get around physically with reasonable safety, and react to our environment intelligently and with pardonable pride. But without the instruction that started a few hours after birth we would not be doing very well. We have needed help from the very beginning — in decreasing amount, to be sure, but nevertheless we have been dependents all our lives. Instincts, such as we attribute to the newly hatched, uncared-for mosquito or house-fly, were not sufficient at our own beginning to keep us alive for a week. When neglected, we could only howl instinctively for nourishment — a very primitive performance. Later a more subtle "howling" for food was taught us, and it is still in use. We now ask for food. That subtlety was a part and product of our training. The house-fly was born with her training completed. She uses not only her own nerve ganglia for the planning and executing of life's operations, making emergency decisions and acting thereon, but she uses also and mainly her generic mind — an equipment that we largely lack. The ratio of the number of our personal decisions to the number that the experience of the human race has built into us is high, because so little is built in; the house-fly, on the other hand, makes some decisions of her own, but mostly uses the inherited mind of thousands of generations of flies.

Terrestrial man's intellectual operations differ only in degree from those of other earthly organisms. If compared honestly with the best responses by the "highest" extra-terrestrial sentient beings, they incite in him small pride.

In view of the width of the cosmos and the slim hold on existence that Nature has provided for Homo sapiens, it would seem properly modest if we talked less about man being superior, less about his being the Annointed of the Gods. Who was annointed, and by whom, we ask, throughout the half billion manless Paleozoic and Mesozoic years when thousands of kinds of wonderful animals sought and fought for survival on the earth? Who was then The Annointed?

Some claimants for human distinction say that man's superiority comes from his "historical sense." They have in mind, probably, the histories written by such as Gibbon, Parkman, and Toynbee. Or thinking a little deeper they also have in mind the word-of-mouth transmission of the unwritten folklore of the past few thousand years. And there is unwritten history, still more basic, in the mother's murmuring of do's and don'ts to her dimly responding infant; she is setting up his "historical sense." But how does this differ, except in degree, from the sparrow chirping to her young, or the worker ants twiddling antennae with the newly emerged callows?

THE
HUMAN
RESPONSE
TO
AN
EXPANDING
UNIVERSE

123

And is not the impelling sex urge of a million kinds of animals one phase of the reciting of the deep and moving history of the ages — reciting it more profoundly, more insistently than it can be done through symbols scratched by us higher and vainer primates on cavern walls, or through the binding of our more systematic scratchings into octavo volumes?

"But only man," you may argue, "*acts* on the basis of his historical knowledge." Again nonsense. In the first place he does not do it very well — goes right on fighting thoughtless, futile wars, goes on acting in a fashion more beastly than angelic. History seems to teach him little. And secondly, after their manner, most animals also act on the basis of experience. The survival of the so-called fittest is a result of an organism's acquired knowledge.

There can be no better laboratory for the elaboration of thoughts on man's orientation in a complex world than a flowering meadow, or a noisy brook, or a spiral galaxy. For the green leaves are sucklings of a star's radiation. The rapids in a brook, responding to universal gravitation, perform erosions of a sort that have worn down to oblivion the lofty pre-Alps and the primitive Appalachians. The 100-ton maple tree that calmly dreams through the decades is in the same functioning universe as the Andromeda Galaxy with its billions of seething stars. The tree heeds the impulse of gravity according to the same rules as those subscribed to by the stars in a globular cluster. Further, the tree is made of the same complex molecular aggregates as are the birds in its branches, the parasites on its roots, and the philosophers who wonder about it.

In a complex situation one simple requirement stands out: we must link ourselves with all the others that participate in life; we must go beyond life and associate ourselves continually and insistently with the solid rocks of the earth, the gaseous winds of the sky.

(Of course, it is our privilege to fancy ourselves as the thinkers and prognosticators for all earthly organisms of the past, present, and future, for all the stars and nebulae, for all the basic entities. It could be one of our hallucinations that we are dominant because we can think and can fashion a pattern for all the world.)

The close student of the social insects would not boast about the superiority of man's social awareness, and he might even qualify his claim for superiority of the human brain. He has seen too much of the wonderful — this student of animal societies. He has seen the honey-bee dance her complex geometry, instructing by sight and scent and diagram her student gatherers of honey and pollen. He has witnessed the magic of many insects carrying out their complicated enterprises.

"But we alone can reason" — that is one of our totally unreasonable assumptions. What evidence is there of thoughtlessness and unreason in the bird choosing its nesting site or a spider locating her web? Their generic minds do much, but thoughtful adjustment to immediate situations does the rest. In contrast, we higher primates are short on inheritance but long on ability to cope with the environmental unusual. A matter of degree or a matter of intensity is here implicated — not a completely different kind of thinking and reasoning. In some characteristics and skills we do not excel; we only approximate the abilities of other animals, and sometimes not very closely. In other characteristics and skills, such as the reading of books, they approach us, but not closely. In differing degrees the higher mammals have all of our virtues and vices, our abilities and futilities.

The teaching of all this is: Do not take man too seriously, even when orienting him among the plants and animals on this local planet, and certainly not when comparing him with the probabilities elsewhere in the richly endowed Metagalaxy.

THE
HUMAN
RESPONSE
TO
AN
EXPANDING
UNIVERSE

125

But let us not tire ourselves with annoyance at man's egocentric vanities. Rather than abuse the presumptuous primate, we should simply call attention to the existence of the generic mind, the most precious inheritance of most animal forms. We point also to the success, over the millions of years, of thousands of animal species that have acquired security by methods that are unknown to us, unknown to animals that must resort, for survival, to mother murmurings, folk tales, and printed history.

Our Limited Sense Organs

As remarked above, the existence of sentient organisms, the natural product of biochemical evolution, must be common all over the universe. From general considerations of planetary origins and the evolution of chemical compounds on a cooling planet's surface, we conclude first that not less than 100 million "high life" locations exist. (The number is probably more like a 100 trillion.) Secondly, that there is no reason for not believing that the biochemical evolution on, let us say, one-half of the suitable planets has attained greater development than we have experienced. Thus, in answer to a common question, we have concluded that we are not alone in this universe, and we have by implication suggested that the Omnipotence (shall we say Nature?) which looks after us has very much else to do. But before we turn to such contemplations, a brief examination of the tools of comprehension is appropriate. Again we may find that our self-esteem is healthily eroded.

The senses of seeing and hearing provide our best methods of ascertaining what is what, and why. The eyes and the ears — without them it would be a strange world. With better eyes and ears, and with additional sense organs, we might have attained to a much finer knowledge than we have had up to now.

The major part of our knowledge of the universe has come through information provided by one sense organ alone — that of vision. Our

human eyes, however, are sensitive only in one small section of the electro-magnetic radiation spectrum. They respond only from the violet to the red — over much less than two octaves. But we have now learned to explore Nature in radiations extending over a range of more than 50 octaves — a range with wave length increasing from the cosmic rays (effectively of less than a billionth of an inch in wave length) through gamma rays, x-rays, and the ultraviolet, on to the blue-to-red radiation that our human eyes record; then from red to heat waves to radio, and on to wave lengths measured in miles.

We know and measure and use these off-color radiations not directly with the retinas of our eyes, as we do with light, but with artifacts, with the retinas, we might say, of photographic plates, Geiger counters, lasers, photo cells, and transistors.

We have done pretty well with the equipment Nature has provided. The eyes and other sense organs arose naturally in the course of evolution and have served animals satisfactorily in the practical problems of existence. They were not designed for use in profound researches into the nature and operations of the cosmos. Practical problems of survival have not until recently included the thirst for "impractical" knowledge. But now our intel-lectual desires have gone ahead of our built-in sensory receptors.

Even when man supplements his sense of vision with a sense of hearing, with poor senses of smell and taste, and a complex of tactile senses, he is still not well equipped to cope with cosmic mysteries. In fact, as an organism ambitious to know, and to know deeply, he is rather primitive in his senses; his primitivism in body anatomy is, of course, generally recog-nized.

Every human sense receptor, except possibly that concerned in tonal discrimination, is out-done by the corresponding receptor of one kind of animal or another — by the hawk's vision, the dog's hearing, the insect's smelling. But these sensory limitations, and the resulting failure to compre-hend fully much of Nature, may be only a local hominid deficiency. On

THE
HUMAN
RESPONSE
TO
AN
EXPANDING
UNIVERSE

127

the basis of the new estimates of the great abundance of stars and the high probability of millions of planets with highly developed life, we are made aware — embarrassingly aware — that we may be intellectual minims in the life of the universe. This uncomfortable idea can be further emphasized by pointing out that sense receptors, in nature quite unknown to us and in fact hardly imaginable, which record phenomena of which we are totally ignorant, may easily exist among the higher sentient organisms on distant planets.

Sometimes we suspect the existence of senses, other than those we recognize in ourselves, among animal and plant forms on this planet — not merely extended ranges of hearing or of vision or of smell, but entirely different responses. The bees and ants respond, as we do not, to polarized light; the birds and fish in migration or in homing respond to what? And there are among us those who speculate about vestigial or embryonic senses hovering around the human psyche.

Growth Through Understanding

To repeat earlier statements: We are primitive in a sensory sense. In spatial location we are incurably peripheral. With help from our star we have slowly evolved out of the wonder-working Archaeozoic ooze in which so many biological experiments have been made. We have arisen from the primeval Hot Thin Soup,* from which also evolved bluebirds and roses, and a million other wonderfully constructed organisms. We must henceforth live with awareness of these cosmic facts and of our ancestry, no matter how disturbing such knowledge is to rigid creeds. We have been, thanks to Darwin, for a century vaguely aware of our immediate anthropoid ancestry. We have been spoken to occasionally about the facts of stars and life, but mostly we do not listen, or act.

The cosmic immensities, whether of space and time, or of outlook and concept, should, however, not dismay us, the local gropers and inter-

* The phase of J. B. S. Haldane.

preters. In our natural program of growth through understanding, each day competes with our yesterdays. Fortunately for us that competition, that striving and groping, is largely inborn, nicely automatic; our succeeding days compete as a matter of course. If care is taken to deal vigorously with the natural regressions that often arise out of static conformity, we shall continue to evolve with the rotating of the planets and the radiating of the suns. We grow naturally with the passage of time, as do the animals and the plants.

But this automatic, slow, slight, and hesitant rising is now not enough for us — the considerably Intelligent and somewhat Informed. We can consciously speed the development. It is not growth in size, or strength, or longevity that should be our goal, but growth primarily in the qualities that we associate with mind, a development that includes those fine undefinables — heart and spirit. And therein lies the nucleus of our cosmic ethic. We have not only the potentiality of conforming to the cosmic theme of Growth, but we can elaborate or revise some of the natural rules. Indeed, each day can and should compete with all the yesterdays of the species.

Humility Comes Naturally

Anthropocentric religions and philosophies, which have so often been conspicuously earthbound and much tangled up with the human mind and human behavior, have in these present days an opportunity for enrichment through incorporating a sensibility of the newly revealed cosmos. If the theologian finds it difficult to take seriously our insistence that the god of humanity is equally the god of gravitation and the god of the spiral galaxies, he may at least be willing to consider the reasonableness of extending to the higher sentient beings that have evolved elsewhere among the myriads of galaxies the same spiritual rating he gives to us. A one-planet deity has for me little appeal.

The new knowledge from many sources — from the test tube, the extended radiation spectrum, the electron microscope, experimental agri-

THE
HUMAN
RESPONSE
TO
AN
EXPANDING
UNIVERSE

129

culture, the radio telescope, the mathematical equations, and the cosmo-trons — the revelations from all these, which were *wholly unknown* to the ancient cosmologists and prophets, make obsolete many of the earlier world views. The new discoveries and developments contribute to the unfolding of a magnificent universe; to be a part thereof and participant therein is also magnificent. With our confrères on distant planets; with our fellow animals and plants of land, sea, and air on this planet; with the rocks and waters of all planetary crusts; and the atoms and photons that make up the stars — with all these we are associated in an existence and an evolution that inspires respect and deep reverence. We cannot escape humility. And as groping philosophers and scientists we are grateful for the mysteries that still lie beyond our present grasp.

There are those who would call this attitude their philosophy, their religion. In their thoughts they would hesitate, I hope, to retreat from the grand galaxies to the parasitic earth; they would be unwilling to come out of the cosmic depths and durations to concern themselves only with one organic species on the crust of one small planet, near a commonplace star, at the edge of one of the myriad galaxies. In their thoughtful search for the Ultimate, let us trust that they get glimpses of a Stellar Theology.

Confessing to Optimism

It seems proper to conclude my discussion on a note of humility and hope, if not of high confidence. Certainly we should be humble about our trivial accomplishment in understanding the total of the external and internal worlds. We know enough to get along, as do most of the other animals. We can cope with all the physical challenges. And going further, we can construct new concepts of beauty and duty.

We assume that the human mind and heart will courageously confront the dangers to mankind as they arise. Our habitation on a fairly steady planet is comfortable on the average, and may get happier. We have increased the length of our useful lives. We have built up ethical systems that tend to bring us safety and satisfaction, but which greatly alarm and dismay us by frequent large-scale failures. We know that the rules of the stars are hard, that the flow of time is irrevocable, that death is dark and will accept no substitutes. But even so, the lights can, if we cooperate, exceed the shadows. The imagination can enter when knowledge falters. We of the higher primates have delved into the cosmic facts deeply enough to recognize the need for cosmic fancies when facts are delayed.

It is my own belief that the central motive of biological existence is to grow in refined complexity, in durability, in adaptability. Man as half beast, half angel, must of course comply with the biogenic common law, but he is able to make amendments thereto.

As rational practitioners of life and elementary interpreters of the cosmos, we oppose superstition — the last stronghold of the irrational — and deny miracles. Thanks to man's experience and reasoning, belief in the supernatural is now tempered with thought. Science has captured many outposts in our necessarily continuous conflict with the Tyranny of the Unknown. We need no longer to appeal to anything beyond Nature when we are confronted by such problems as the origin of life, or the binding forces of nucleons, or the orbits in a star cluster, or the electrochemical dynamics of a thought. We can assail all such questions rationally.

It is probable, and certainly is deeply desired, that the men of the future will correct our shortcomings and build on the basis of our thoughts and acts a finer mental and social structure — one that is in better balance with Nature's heavy investment in the locally dominant human race.

THE
HUMAN
RESPONSE
TO
AN
EXPANDING
UNIVERSE

131

Index